Conquering Stress

by

KRS Edstrom, M.S.

DEDICATION

To my parents, Mary and Ev Edstrom

KRS Edstrom, M.S., is a HealthStyle consultant, speaker and head of the MCA/Universal Fitness Program. Her company, Get Motivated by KRS, helps individuals and corporations stay motivated and achieve their HealthStyle goals. KRS is a member of the Association for Fitness in Business.

All inquiries should be addressed to:
Barron's Educational Series, Inc.
250 Wireless Boulevard
Hauppauge, New York 11788

Library of Congress Catalog Card No. 92-26960

International Standard Book No. 0-8120-4837-7

Library of Congress Cataloging-in-Publication Data

Edstrom, KRS
Conquering stress / by KRS Edstrom.
p. cm. — (Barron's business success series)
"Barron's a business success guide."
Includes bibliographies and index.
ISBN 0-8120-4837-7
1. Stress management. 2. Middle managers—Job stress. I. Title.
II. Series
RA785.E38 1992
155.9'042—dc20 92-26960
CIP

PRINTED IN THE UNITED STATES OF AMERICA

3456 5500 987654321

CONTENTS

Introduction, by Paul J. Rosch, M.D., F.A.C.P. v

Foreword vii

Preface viii

PART I: Getting to Know the Enemy: *What Is Stress?* 1

CHAPTER 1 Stress Today 1

CHAPTER 2 Stress Hurts You Whether You Know It or Not 11

CHAPTER 3 Four Things that Shape Your Stress 21

CHAPTER 4 Hard Work Never Killed Anybody—But Stress Has 37

PART II: Making Friends with the Enemy: *The Solution to Stress* 49

CHAPTER 5 The Plan of Attack 49

CHAPTER 6 How to Achieve "Stress Success" in Your Job 61

CHAPTER 7 Stress-Conquering Skills 67

CHAPTER 8 Nine External Stress-Conquering Skills and Tips 71

CHAPTER 9 Five Internal Stress-Conquering Skills 79

CHAPTER 10 Psychological Skills for Conquering Stress 91

Summary 97

Additional Resources 99

Index 100

INTRODUCTION

A 1983 cover story in *Time* magazine labeled stress "The Epidemic of the 80s," and recent surveys confirm that the problem has markedly increased in the past decade. Why all the sudden fuss? After all, stress has been around since Adam and Eve were in the garden of Eden. Is it because there is more stress today? Is contemporary stress somehow more harmful? Or is it due to the fact that recent research can explain the mechanisms of stress-related illness, confirming what were previously merely anecdotal reports or old wives' tales?

The answer is a resounding "yes" to each of these questions. Job stress is a major factor. However, children, senior citizens, and housewives also suffer from more and different kinds of stress than existed decades ago because of other disruptive sociocultural changes. For many, stress has become such an ingrained part of daily life that its adverse effects on physical and emotional health are simply taken for granted.

As pointed out in this easy-to-understand book, stress is an unavoidable consequence of life. However, there are some stresses you can do something about, and others you can't hope to avoid. The trick is in being able to distinguish between the two. Experiencing grief and sorrow for months after the death of a loved one is normal. But spending the rest of your life in mourning serves no useful purpose. On the other hand, if what should be a fifteen-minute drive to and from work takes you more than an hour every day, it's possible you could do something about it. You might go to your superior and explain that you are not being as productive as you could be, and that everyone would benefit if you could come in and leave an hour earlier to avoid the traffic jams.

Separate the stresses in your life into those you can't avoid or influence, and those you can. In that way, you can devote your time and talent to areas where you can achieve results, rather than being constantly frustrated, like Don Quixote tilting at windmills. And for unavoidable stress, if you can't fight and you can't flee, sometimes you have to learn to flow.

Conquering Stress goes a long way toward explaining this in simple language. It is filled with practical examples, including illustrations of how three successful CEOs manage their personal stress at work and at home. In addition to helping you learn how to recognize sources of stress in your life, this attractive volume offers a variety of useful tips and techniques you can utilize in reducing the harmful effects of stress. It correctly emphasizes that stress is different for each of us, which is why it is so difficult for scientists to agree on a satisfactory definition. However, everyone concurs that the sense or feeling of being out of control is always distressful. Often, this is due to faulty perceptions that we can learn to correct.

This concise presentation provides the tools that will help you conquer stress so you can become more productive, more fulfilled, and enjoy an all-around higher quality of life.

Paul J. Rosch, M.D., F.A.C.P.
President, The American Institute of Stress

Clinical Professor of Medicine and Psychiatry
New York Medical College

Adjunct Clinical Professor of Medicine in Psychiatry
University of Maryland School of Medicine

FOREWORD

When I accepted the offer to write this book, the title that flashed across my mind was "If I can do it, you can do it." For 23 years I tried everything from valium to stress workshops in an attempt to quell the stress monster. But in trying to figure a way *out* of stress, my greatest learning ironically came from diving *into* it. I found that my challenge was not in focusing on the external world, but in addressing the internal world; a matter of self-mastery more than the control of outside factors. In this book, I have combined the results of my personal experience along with my professional experience and study. I hope you benefit.

As the book was to be work-world related, I decided to include the personal stories and tips of three CEOs from diverse businesses (food, exercise, and entertainment) with household names. Thus my choices: Russ Hanlin, CEO, Sunkist; Augie Nieto, CEO, Life Fitness; and Meyer Gottlieb, CEO, Samuel Goldwyn (Hollywood film company).

Busy as they are, I found these men generous with their time, full of life, and full of incredible experiences. I hope their stories will inspire you to get serious about conquering stress so that you can better get on with enjoying the process of living.

KRS

PREFACE

You Are, to Some Extent, What You Do

Whatever effect your job has on you is carried into the rest of your life. Unfortunately, most of us regularly experience job stress. One survey revealed that 75 percent of Americans described their jobs as stressful. In 1991 a shocking one-third (34 percent) of us even considered quitting our jobs because of stress! This means most of us are carrying a great deal of stress home each night, which is not exactly a health "plus." In fact, many authorities consider job stress the major adult health problem today.

- Almost 90 percent of us experience high levels of stress at least once a week.
- Seventy-five to 90 percent of all visits to primary-care physicians are for stress-related disorders.

And it's not getting any better. *The Mitchum Report on Stress in the 90s* says that most Americans report being under much more stress now than five years ago.

- Every week, 112 million people take medication for stress-related symptoms.
- According to a recent nationwide poll, medications for stress-related headaches comprised 61 percent of all over-the-counter medications.
- The top three prescription drugs are for stress-related, *preventable*, conditions.

Stress Costs You Money

Job stress is costing industry (and therefore you) a lot of money. Look at these facts:

- Job stress costs American industry more than $200

billion a year in absenteeism, lost productivity, accidents, and medical insurance.
- Of all industrial accidents, 60 to 80 percent are due to stress incurred by workers.

A sobering seven in ten workers say job stress causes frequent health problems. Job stress accounts for more than one-half of the 550,000,000 work days lost annually because of absenteeism. Workers say their companies are responsible for their stress and they want compensation. Eighty-two percent think that burnout victims deserve disability pay from their employers. And apparently they are getting it—in epidemic portions.

Consequently, industry is suffering. Each case costs employers and insurers an average of $73,270 for disability payments. Industry complains that while some suits may be valid, everyone is jumping on the money wagon and claiming anything and everything as stress related.

Thankfully, stress reduction efforts have recently become the leading priority for employee-assistance programs. Almost two-thirds of all work sites with 750 employees or more now have stress control projects under way. By giving people permission to express themselves about stress and by educating them as to how to overcome it, stress is taken "out of the closet." This is a powerful first step, since the denial of stressful states and the inability to express emotions are associated with increased risk of stress-related illness.

WHAT THIS BOOK WILL DO FOR YOU

This book will help you conquer stress, whether you work for yourself or somebody else, whether you work at a hot dog stand or at a Fortune 500 company.

Conquering Stress is about releasing you from the grip of stress by developing effective, new internal and external Stress-Conquering skills. You'll find the internal skills particularly powerful because, in conquering the internal world, much of the external world falls into place.

You will also learn valuable tips to outsmart stress. The point is not that you become an expert on stress statistics but that you learn to experience and react to stress in a new way. Combining information with the Stress-Conquering skills is the key to making a friend out of what has long been perceived as an enemy.

What you learn about conquering stress in your work world applies directly to your personal life as well as to the rest of the world. Each affects the other. Your work environment is essentially an enlarged version, a macrocosm, of the family system, from relationship issues to power struggles. Similarly, your place of work is a smaller version, a microcosm, of the rest of the world.

This book will help you conquer stress in three basic ways: 1) Increase your "stress literacy" by providing the latest information along with KRS Edstrom's personal study and experience; 2) give you effective Stress-Conquering skills; and 3) provide inspiration by showing how a few prominent CEOs handle the stress of success.

THANKS

Thanks to my own personal "de-stressors," advisors, and/or supporters: My parents whose influence could fill a book and whose continuous love keeps me upright; my sisters and brother, whose phone talks are always quality entertainment; Glenn Vinzant, whose constant support and advice are deeply appreciated; Shinzen Young, who is the inspiration behind the "master your self, master stress" message and a brilliant meditation/life teacher. Other important friends: Pat Britten, Usharbudh Arya, Jeff Harrington, Teresa James, Terry Wilson, Marcy Calhoun, Mike Dougherty, Bill Stark, and Linda Dozoretz (who encouraged me to take this project); my clients Skip Heinecke, John Koenig, David May, Naomi Feldman, and Jan Wood (MCA/Universal). And a bunny named Lassiter.

PART I: GETTING TO KNOW THE ENEMY: WHAT IS STRESS?

CHAPTER 1 STRESS TODAY

"It's always appeared to me that stress is within the individual and not manufactured by the situation."

—Russ Hanlin, CEO, Sunkist

Stress is nothing new. It has been around as long as Adam's traumatic apple dilemma, or the Big Bang, whichever way you prefer. Formal stress research is not quite as old but does have a substantive 80 year history—a time span that is unfortunately not reflected in the progress made. In 1914 Walter Cannon came up with what he called the fight or flight response, two natural reactions to acute stressors. A few years later Hans Selye, an endocrinologist at the University of Montreal, went a step further in studying people (and animals) in stressful situations. Unfortunately most of his work, like Cannon's, was with extremely traumatic situations such as a war crisis. Not until the 60s did "natural catastrophes" like divorce, illness, or death get any attention.

A scale of stress was developed by researchers Holmes and Rahe in 1967. These men were interested in the correlation between the amount of change in people's lives and their risk of illness. Their scale was based on the theory that the body does not like surprises, or sudden changes in routine, whether pleasant or unpleasant. They compiled an arbitrary list of stressors in order of severity, with death of a spouse worth

100 points, followed by other stressors such as divorce, marital separation, and going to jail. While "common denominator" stress may exist, the scale doesn't take into account individual differences in reacting to stress.

Everyone reacts uniquely to different stressors. Sunkist CEO Russ Hanlin agrees, believing that stress is individual and is defined primarily from within. "I've witnessed people in seemingly unstressful occupations that had what we would identify as stress-related illnesses," he says. He continues, "On the other hand, I have seen people who have had nervous breakdowns who have not been in particularly stressful situations."

How is stress defined today? For one thing, definitions have become more individualized. One popular definition is to say that stress is what each person *thinks* it is—or isn't. For example, the sight of a dog may send one person into a panic while relaxing another. In this sense, even the ultimate stressor—death—can be perceived as stressful or unstressful. (It is said that death can be a wonderfully peaceful, even enlightening experience if greeted with complete awareness and acceptance.)

Today every manifestation of stress, mental as well as physical, however subtle or gross, requires recognition and attention. We no longer have to pretend symptoms don't exist or try to hide them from others.

Pay heed to your feelings. If something is bothering you, but it's not on somebody's scale of stressors, it still counts. I've had many clients try to invalidate their physical or emotional stress, or feel guilty for being stressed, because they thought, "This doesn't bother other people, so it shouldn't be bothering me. Something must be wrong with me." Ironically, reacting with guilt can exacerbate the stress and become a stressor itself.

As a HealthStyle motivation consultant, I saw a 26-year-old record executive client who was shocked and intimidated by his first backache. "What's happening to me? Is it a pinched nerve or maybe a disc out of place?" he asked, with I-know-I'm-going-to-die eyes. Realizing he was unnecessarily scaring himself with frightening buzz words he had unconsciously collected and stored away for just such an occasion, I assured him that it was just a little muscle tightness, probably from hitting his golf club differently. I promised him his nerves and discs were just fine and advised him to take a hot bath, do some slow stretches, and relax. The next day he called and said, "Thanks. My backache is gone." He then added a little sheepishly, "I think just the assurance that it was nothing serious helped the most." In changing his *thinking* about his stress-induced pain, it went away. Conversely, had he continued to allow his infectious thoughts to infiltrate his body, he might very well have ended up in a doctor's office the following day. Virgins to stress and pain are refreshingly receptive to work with because they have not grooved a lifetime of erroneous ideas and reactions.

Stress affects everybody and it kills us as relentlessly as cancer—and in greater numbers. Then why has relatively little been done on global, national, or individual levels to reduce stress? Perhaps because we are only now beginning to prove on a more scientific (and thus acceptable) level, the damage caused by stress.

Stress needs to be redefined on a general as well as a personal level. Once we clearly define it we can better overcome it. Once we get to know the enemy, it no longer *is* the enemy.

WE ARE OVER STIMULATED

In fully understanding stress, we must not discount the effect outside factors have on us. Technology, for example, may very well have given us too much too fast. The electronic era and faster deadlines keep many of us in a state of constant stimulation. Most of us are subjected to overload on a daily basis. The former optimistic definition of *progress* has become distorted. It seems we have unknowingly sacrificed real progress, internal progress, for our frantic, almost compulsive, urge to expand externally. Speed is an accepted way of life, especially if one is interested in "getting somewhere." In this sense, speed has replaced true progress and for many, life has become a race without a finish line.

WHY YOU RUN OUT OF ENERGY

Did nature provide us with any protection against stress? Yes, according to Hans Selye. In fact, Selye came up with something called GAS—a scientific theory known as the General Adaptation Syndrome. GAS means that our bodies have a built-in ability to adapt to stress—to a certain degree; after that, stress occurs. According to Selye, it doesn't matter if the demand made is pleasant (such as a wedding or vacation) or unpleasant, but rather if the *demand for adaptation* is too great.

What's so wrong with living with stress day after day? Very simply, the well runs dry. We get worn out and, in a sense, die from lack of energy. (Some days I think I know what that feels like.) The adrenaline that is so useful in short-term situations can, in extreme situations, actually run out. This is called adrenaline insufficiency and can lead to death. At best, our adrenal glands get tired and so do we. Many scientists believe that stress hormones quicken the aging process. Aging could thus be defined as the wind down of our adaptation energy from the ongoing demands of life. We were simply not designed to endure endless punishment. (You will learn skills to help offset this depletion in Part II.)

Adaptation energy is finite and stress depletes its resources. You may have noticed that older people are often less flexible and more easily stressed. They sort of scale down their capacity to endure stress. A whole day can revolve tensely around the stress of getting a letter mailed, for example.

The thing to remember is that when stress is short term, we can handle it. Stress hormones take over quite efficiently; they strengthen your immune system and help your body resist disease. After the stress subsides, your body automatically turns the hormones off. Many modern day stresses however, are long-term, no-win situations, such as an ongoing high pressure job, and are a different matter; they can significantly upset the biochemical balances in your body. These imbalances can, in turn, impair your immune system and leave you open to invasions of cancer cells and dangerous infections.

Homeostasis is the word coined by early stress researcher Walter Cannon to describe the physiological balance that is so important to our good health. He knew that brain-body communication must be in sync since the brain (specifically the hypothalamus) is where the body gets its orders to react.

Biochemical imbalances induced by stress include the release of anabolic and catabolic hormones in uneven amounts. When these don't balance a harmful stage is set. Anabolic hormones are the good guys and are considered regenerative by nature, helping to replace certain cells such as white blood cells that fight infection and the cells in the lining of the digestive system that are important in protecting against ulcers. Catabolic hormones include cortisol and adrenaline, which are released during stress and can be helpful in small doses for short periods. Prolonged doses are harmful to your internal organs and immune system, and cause fatigue, hypertension, raised cholesterol, and some even think arteriosclerosis.

Understanding the concept of this very basic life force energy system will hopefully motivate you to preserve your precious energy reserves. By becoming skilled in the techniques described later on, you can better extend the life expectancy of your adaptation energy and of *you*. Best of all, you will be less stressed in the process.

CAN STRESS BE POSITIVE?

Technically not. *Webster's* says stress is "any mental or physical tension or strain"—words that don't fit very comfortably in the same sentence with *good* or *positive*. But the definition of stress has been revised over the years, beginning with Selye himself, who concocted the word *eustress* to mean stress that is positive. This terminology represents a linguistical contradiction as well as a physiological one—different things happen in your body with positive and negative (stressful) experiences (they are two different things).

Accepting a term like *positive stress* also makes it too easy for certain personalities, workaholics, for example, to rationalize their stress by saying, "Yes, I'm stressed but it's probably good stress, so I'll keep going."

The idea of managing stress or coping with stress also strikes a wrong chord with me, especially when it is presented as the solution to stress. It is not a solution; at best it is a way of getting through tension or strain. Sort of as you might cope with a wart on the end of your nose. Rather than thinking in terms of the coping, hold-your-breath-until-it's-over notion of stress, let's consider the concept of reacting to stress in a whole new way and, in that sense, of conquering stress.

A study I conducted of America's top CEOs for my book *Healthy, Wealthy & Wise* shows that these leaders often think of commonly viewed stressors as challenges rather than negative experiences. How do you know when something is a challenge or a stressor? I asked several CEOs that very question. The CEO of Samuel Goldwyn, Meyer Gottlieb, answered without hesitation. "Simple. One motivates [a positive challenge] and one debilitates [stress]."

Augie Nieto, CEO of Life Fitness (makers of Lifecycle and other break-through fitness equipment), also had a quick answer. Augie says that an experience that is positive provides "the energy that puts you on the edge." He continues, "Negative stress is when you go *over* the edge. That's the balance. You want the sensitivity to be on your tiptoes, but you don't want to fall over."

For most people, a situation is usually positive and healthful when it's enjoyable, challenging, and includes elements of progress and control. Augie is an entrepreneur by nature. He started his Life Fitness business as a college student 14 years ago and can now, at the tender age of 34, boast of it being the largest computerized equipment manufacturer in the world. He says that as a kid, the process of building a business wasn't stressful, it was fun. Today his main concern is to keep it as challenging as it was when he was building his business. Standing still stresses Augie. "Business without growth is boring," he says.

Meyer Gottlieb agrees. "Half the time you have stress because you don't think you're busy enough. It's 'How many things can I do at the same time?' It's a little bit of a game."

Like the others, Russ Hanlin, CEO of Sunkist, describes what many would label stress as his form of recreation. He says, "I have days when I go from one meeting to another and important things are happening and people are stacked up outside waiting to see me…I get exhilarated by that."

When you're in control and things are progressing as you want, the experience is a positive, enjoyable challenge. When you're not in control, and you're in over your head, the experience is negative and is what I call stress. Stress has various degrees for individuals; it's not always a case of black and white and it is different for each person. It is important that you are clear about what stress is and what stress isn't so you can better understand your personal stress gauge, respect it, and then work to expand it.

HOOKED ON STRESS

Another problem with the concept of positive stress is stress addiction. Some of us are actually hooked on the adrenaline "rush" of stress but, by calling it positive stress, it becomes acceptable and even healthy sounding. This is a modern day phenomenon—cave men never came to crave the after-glow sensations of being chased by wild animals. But when imminent death was removed from the scene, as with modern day "survivable disaster" stress, the accompanying rush became more alluring. Some find this rush in bungee jumping, some find it in gambling, and some find it in their work. The harm comes when one becomes hooked on the rush and neglects other aspects of his life in the process.

Stress author Rosalind Forbes says that some people thrive on stress and consistently choose activities that make them feel excited. They also see stress as a driving force behind their major accomplishments. She calls these people "stress seekers." Stress underload is actually a problem for stress addicts. They commonly get migraines on Sundays when the stress lets up—just the opposite of other people. People often find it difficult to distinguish between what is referred to as a little polite positive stress and big bad stress addiction. Just because you crave an adrenaline high in the form of stress, don't kid yourself that it's a passion for your work. Alcoholics also crave a kind of high that eventually causes their demise. Caution should be used when using adrenaline as a drug; remember, it is expendable.

DO YOU KNOW WHEN YOU ARE STRESSED?

Newer definitions of stress require more clear-cut distinctions. I break stress into two categories: cognitive stress and noncognitive stress. Cognitive stress is stress you are aware of. You know, for example, that your unreasonable boss is causing your headache. Noncognitive stress is a bit more insidious. You are not conscious of the stress or you may deny it on some level. You keep working, keep pushing on, not acknowledging the source of your headache. It often takes a "hammer over your head" (in the form of a more serious illness) to get your attention. Even then, many will miss the cause-and-effect point. Unfortunately, most of us experience sickness, disease, and stress without learning the lesson they were meant to deliver. Thus, we just repeat unhealthy patterns again and again.

I'm not alone in observing that people often unconsciously opt to be sick or stressed rather than deal with the underlying problems of their illness. Learn to acknowledge when and where you are stressed. You must turn noncognitive stress into cognitive stress before you can fully conquer stress.

Everyone reacts differently to different stressful stimuli, so who can most accurately define your personal stress? Selye? Me? The answer, of course, is a stress-literate *you*.

CHAPTER 2

STRESS HURTS YOU WHETHER YOU KNOW IT OR NOT

"When the mind suffers, the body cries out."

Whether you acknowledge stress or not, stress upsets your body chemistry in very dramatic and potentially life-threatening ways. But if so much stress is internal, how do you know if and when you are stressed? What are the physical, mental, and emotional symptoms of stress?

Physical Signs of Stress Include:

Things you can see or feel

- Heart rate increases
- Sweating increases
- Muscles tense
- Pupils dilate
- Respiration rate and pattern is altered

Things you cannot immediately see or feel

- Immune system is weakened
- Endocrine balance is disrupted
- Blood pressure rises
- Digestion slows down
- Blood clots more readily
- Blood sugar rises
- Bowel and bladder muscles loosen

Most of you are probably quite familiar with at least some of these symptoms and are perhaps relieved to give them a name and know that you are not alone in experiencing them.

But what if you don't care whether your pupils dilate and you sweat a little? After all, that's why we have deoderant, right? Yes, the symptoms of stress have given birth to many wonderful stress Band-Aid inventions over the years. The catch is that many symptoms, left with only a Band-Aid, eventually lead to illness, disease, and even death.

STRESS CAN KILL YOU—OR WORSE, GIVE YOU A COLD

Understanding that stress can and does kill people and is probably responsible for many symptoms you have already experienced is an important step in overcoming stress. But before we talk about skills to conquer stress (Part II), let me motivate you a little further.

Directly or indirectly, stress is known to be a main contributor to six of the leading causes of death in the United States. Accidental injuries and suicide are included in the list. In fact, a shocking 50 to 80 percent of all disease is considered stress related, or *psychosomatic* (psycho = mind; soma = body)!

Stress-related Diseases and Disorders Include:

- Heart disease
- Cancer
- Asthma
- Diabetes
- Migraine headaches
- Stomach ulcers
- Arthritis
- Genital herpes
- High blood pressure
- Psoriasis
- Obesity

- Infertility
- Impotence
- Respiratory diseases (bronchitis and emphysema)
- Chronic low back pain

The American Academy of Orthopedic Surgeons says that 80 percent of us will experience at least one episode of significant back pain in our lives. Do you think 80 percent of us, if x-rayed, would truly show that our bad backs are caused genetically? My guess is no. Our back pain is more likely a manifestation of our stress. It may be more accurate to say that 80 percent of us manifest stress in the form of significant back pain at some point in our lives.

The *New England Journal of Medicine* reported that high levels of stress make you two times as likely to develop a cold (five different viruses tested the same). The reason for this is most probably that stress weakens the immune system and thus leaves the system defenseless against cold viruses. I'm always surprised to observe the look on audience faces when I pop this bit of news. When I list the major stress-related killers like heart disease and cancer, I often see blank faces, but when I mention that stress contributes to *colds* I get a visible reaction, like, "Hey, wait a minute, heart disease is one thing but a cold is getting pretty close to home." I think the reason for this response may be that none of us really believes we're going to get a major disease (or die), but we all *know* we are going to get knock-out colds. It's one of life's few predictables.

LOWER YOUR STRESS TO LOWER YOUR CHOLESTEROL

Probably no word in the last decade has motivated more people to be concerned about their health than cholesterol. The food industry has built entire marketing campaigns around the "our product has no (or low) cholesterol" theme. Foods that never even had cholesterol are given health banners and paraded down Main Street: "Eat plenty of Jell-O®—it's cholesterol free!"

I'm not above resorting to "cheap cholesterol tactics" to make my point about stress, especially when science is on my side. In fact, tests now indicate that stress can increase cholesterol levels. The liver apparently produces more cholesterol when under stress and the body also tends to hang onto fat when stressed.

A quick precautionary word about wine and cholesterol-lowering claims. Many people have been overjoyed to hear claims that, in moderate amounts, wine can lower cholesterol. Claims like this unnerve me because they tend to give people medicinal license to drink. Russ Hanlin of Sunkist and I chuckled at the possible humorous scenarios. At one point he joked, "My answer for claims that wine can lower your cholesterol is that a damaged liver doesn't produce cholesterol."

IT'S NOT "ALL IN YOUR HEAD"

So what is this connection between the mind and the body, between what we think and how we feel? One fancy, relatively new word for the mind-body connection is psychoneuroimmunology, a word that was based on a hotly debated study of the 1980s that showed certain infection-fighting white blood cells were less numerous in people who were depressed or bereaved. In a rather large nutshell: Outside factors influence psychological phenomena, which affect our brains, which affect our neurochemistry, which affects our neuroendocrine systems, which affect our immune systems, which affect our health, which can cause disease, which can cause death. In a little smaller nutshell: the mind can kill the body.

From one perspective, stress is in your body, as we've discussed. But from another, stress is "all in your head," in the sense that many aspects of stress are monitored from the brain. Unfortunately, in its usual negative context, "it's all in your head" connotes self blame and delivers an inaccurate and unnecessary message of guilt. The word psychosomatic is still too frequently used in a derogatory context:

"Clyde is sick again?"

"Well, sort of. It's, you know, psychosomatic..."

"Oh, I see, nothing serious."

While this mind-body connection has become more popular in recent years, it is not exactly hot-off-the-press, New Age information. Aristotle was probably the first to express the concept of the mind-body connection, that they affect each other and can even talk in a two-way conversation. He prophetized, "Soul and body, I suggest, react sympathetically upon each other. A change in the state of the soul produces a change in the shape of the body. A change in the shape of the body produces a change in the state of the soul." Translation for our purposes: a sick or stressed body produces a sick or stressed state of mind and vice versa. In fact, just visualizing a stressful situation can create the same chemical reactions as the real thing. Negative thoughts have similar effects. The good news is that stress conquering skills and positive reprogramming can reverse these chemical reactions and have proven quite effective in combating stress-related disorders.

THE "MIND FLU"

The physical symptoms of stress are often quite blatant. Ulcers, for example, are pretty hard to ignore. The mental and emotional symptoms of stress, however, can be a bit more nebulous. More nebulous, perhaps, but equally undesirable. When you are stressed, your life commonly feels unpredictable, uncontrollable, and overwhelming. You may feel a range of emotions such as frustration or anger, or you may just shut down and not feel anything. My cousin Bill calls the psychological symptoms of stress the "Mind Flu." I like that name because it legitimizes our feelings in a humorous way. By the time "I've got the Mind Flu" is out of my mouth (or his) we are both laughing and the momentum of the dreaded flu is already broken. Similarly, being aware of the symptoms of mental and emotional stress helps break their momentum.

Mental and Emotional Signs of Stress Include:

- Depression
- Anxiety
- Nervous exhaustion
- Disorientation
- Feelings of inadequacy
- Loss of self-esteem
- Lowered tolerance for ambiguity
- Apathy
- Loss of achievement motivation
- Increased irritability

IS YOUR PERSONALITY DISEASE PRONE?

According to many, the disease your body "selects" depends on your personality. When a certain personality experiences a certain ongoing stress response, a predictable disorder will result. I want to elaborate briefly on this fascinating subject for the purpose of further demonstrating the powerful effect of our thoughts, behavior, and personality on our bodies.

Listed below are some common diseases. Under each disease are listed personality characteristics commonly associated with it. Note that many of these characteristics are stress inducing, in and of themselves, which naturally perpetuates the personality–disease cycle. You may know somebody who has the conditions listed below or you may have them yourself. In any case, you might find it interesting to compare personality with disease.

Rheumatoid Arthritis

Common personality characteristics:

- Inhibited and conforming, self-conscious, shy
- Suppress negative emotions
- Frequently overly righteous and moralistic
- Self-sacrificing, masochistic
- Perfectionistic

Migraine

Common personality characteristics:

- Obsessive-compulsive (compensate by taking on more than they can do during work and leisure; try too hard and self destruct in the process)
- Low self-worth (want desperately to be loved and admired)
- Can be rigid, intolerant of others
- Fanatical
- Self-righteous
- Perfectionistic
- Repress emotions
- Accident prone

Ulcers

Common personality characteristics:

- Dependent
- Internalize hostility
- Extremely sensitive to stress
- Sexual problems

Heart attack

Common personality characteristics:

- Aggressive
- Impatient
- Self-disciplined

- Competitive
- High need for achievement
- Discomfort with leisure time

Cancer

(The following list of personality characteristics includes the research of Lawrence LeShan, former Chief of the Psychology Department at the Institute of Applied Biology in New York, in 1956, the Simontons' work in 1975, and Joan Arehart-Treichel's recent report in her book *Biotypes*.)

- Depressed
- Feel undeserving of love, poor self-image, depends on others for validation of worth
- Needs of others come first, compulsive giver
- Tendency toward self-pity
- Difficulty in forgiving others
- Self-dislike
- Feel rejected
- Repress their feelings
- Dream less
- Dissatisfied with their work
- Experience more life stress
- Inability to express hostility
- Maternal domination
- Tension in relationship with mother and/or father
- Immature sexual adjustment

What exactly is the relationship between stress and cancer? As I said, symptoms like those listed above are stress inducing, and stress has been found to impair our immune system's ability to recognize and destroy cancer cells. One is in a weakened state mentally and physically, which is a fertile ground for the growth of cancer cells.

Interestingly, one researcher described the cancer candidate as feeling weak, with unworthiness as his true state. Depression is said to predate and be a common-denominator among cancer patients. One expert described cancer as "despair experienced at a cellular level." I have even heard cancer described as a socially acceptable way of committing suicide (the ultimate stress). I was shocked when I learned that many patients don't even take their cancer medication. One study showed that in 60 percent of chemotherapy patients there was no trace of the prescribed medication in their blood samples! Mind-body author Bernie Siegel, M.D., says 15 to 20 percent of patients actually want to die to escape life's problems and only 15 to 20 percent play an active role in their survival.

This small percentage most probably enjoys the feeling of being in charge of their own lives, in the most literal sense. You can do the same by learning to monitor and control your reactions to stress. It's exciting when you realize that ultimately, you can have more control over your body and mind than any doctor.

When one considers the strong, ever-evolving link between personality, stress, and disease, dealing with stress becomes more critical than just making those tough days at the office a little easier. It becomes a matter of survival to get a handle on stress. It also becomes apparent that the antidote goes beyond a trip to your local M.D. for a "fix it" pill. It requires reflection and action on our part and a willingness to change.

Being an expert in stress history or human biochemistry is not a prerequisite in conquering stress. You simply must acknowledge that stress harms your mind and body, whether you are aware of it or not. You can then take the Four Steps to No Stress discussed in Chapter 5.

CHAPTER 3

FOUR THINGS THAT SHAPE YOUR STRESS

"The mind can make a hell of heaven or a heaven of hell."

—Nietzsche

We now know that stress is not just a bad day at work or a traffic jam. We know that more subtle things like personality characteristics can cause stress and that increased stress can lead to various diseases. I now want to broaden our scope a bit to include other possible factors that can affect your level of stress.

The interesting thing about stress is that while it can be difficult to categorize because it is different for everyone, it is not nebulous at all. As with individualized diet and exercise programs, there are just four basic areas that need to be addressed in conquering stress:

1. Genetics—biological and innate personality characteristics
2. Environment—controllable and uncontrollable external conditions
3. Psychological—including mental and emotional characteristics formed early in life
4. Personal paradigms—your perception of the world based on the first three factors

Which of these is most important? Depending on whom you ask, it can be a controversial and even political point. Some believe that our perceptions of stress are shaped by biological factors, while others believe that our perceptions are influenced by psychosocial factors. Depending on consensus, the direction for future research and funding, for example, would vary. One would require pharmacological intervention ("take a pill") and the other would indicate psychological work and lifestyle changes.

One theory says that we each have inborn unchangeable differences in our potential for adaptation to stress; we should therefore focus on changeable factors, like our environment, that are the apparent *origins* of stress. I agree that we have an inborn tolerance for stress but I also know that this tolerance can be expanded—it *is* changeable. Thus, not just one neat answer, but a combination of approaches is needed.

The genetic and environmental factors that affect stress are relatively self explanatory. I will therefore focus a bit more on the psychological and personal paradigm factors, as they are the ones people are most unfamiliar with. They also have an exciting potential to change your life in a significant way.

GENETICS Are You at the Mercy of Your Genes?

> *"The worst day I can think of is a day lying on the beach."*
>
> *—Russ Hanlin, CEO, Sunkist*

Genetic influences on our perceptions of stress include the physical biology as well as personality characteristics with which you were born. While one theory says we select our own parents for the lessons we need to learn, suffice it to say that we must take what we get and work from there.

We are born with a unique physiology that results in, among other things, our own particular predisposed neurological response to stress. Some of us are designed with "tuned-up" rabbit-like reflexes to life and some with cat-sleeping-in-the-sun-like tendencies.

One could go through the entire body, part by part, and hypothesize how particular strengths and weaknesses might react differently to particular stressors. Why, for example, does stress affect one person's stomach and another's back? Individual manifestations of stress can depend on, among other things, one's genes.

Innate personality characteristics are other genetic factors to consider. For example, some experts now think 30 percent of Type A personalities (driven, impatient) are biologically inherited. A few of the CEOs I interviewed for this book fall into this 30 percent category but have become what I call balanced Type As. They like things fast and exciting, but no longer let them run their lives.

Russ Hanlin, CEO of Sunkist, is a great example. Russ says he was probably born Type A. He says, "When I'm standing still I've got this physical energy that has to be released. I'm not nervous, it's just excess energy." He laughs again as he continues, "It's like when you see a seven-year-old boy sitting in a chair twitching all over." Russ rather enjoys his energy but admits, "I suppose I drive people nuts, particularly at home. It wouldn't be unusual for me to be reading the paper and watching television at the same time, then get up and play the piano during commercials."

Biorhythms are another variable that apparently comes with the genetic package. There are said to be physical, emotional, and intellectual biorhythm cycles of high and low points, during which we function better or worse. Experts say stress happens most frequently in the low points of one's cycles. Whether or not you buy that, you most probably are aware that you have high points and low points in the day: times when you feel revved up to exercise, times that are better or worse for thought processing, and times of stress.

This is just a peek at how your genes play a role in defining stress. While you may not have a say in the genetic hand you were dealt, there are many things you can do to transform that hand.

ENVIRONMENT Are You at the Mercy of Your Environment?

Environmental factors that affect stress are relatively obvious but are ever-increasing and must be identified in defining your stress. Some are controllable to various degrees, others are not. Extreme weather conditions, for example, are completely uncontrollable. Just ask Russ Hanlin, CEO of Sunkist. In the winter of 1989 they lost more than half of their crop as the result of a freeze. Thousands of growers and packing houses had to shut down, and according to Russ, "Every plan—advertising, sales promotion, marketing plans—everything we were doing in this company was suddenly gone." They had to recast their plans and their budget and were forced to lay off hundreds of people, which, for Russ, was the worst part. "To lay off an otherwise satisfactory employee because of a weather disaster is a very, very tough thing to do," he says, "but you realize that if you don't do it you jeopardize all remaining jobs. The company is weakened and perhaps fails because of your inability or unwillingness to take the proper action. You have to do what maintains the institution for the future."

Life Fitness CEO Augie Nieto says as far as his business is concerned, external factors are more frustrating than internal ones because "external factors you have no control of," adding "such as the recession or a trend away from exercising into drinking beer, for example."

Meyer Gottlieb, CEO of Hollywood film company Samuel Goldwyn, also finds external stressors frustrating. Meyer laughs as he explains, "We're in a crisis every Monday morning, every time we release a picture. We have to make a lot of decisions and a lot of money is spent. "But," he clarifies, "because we are in control of those decisions, it's not really a crisis. You keep your fingers crossed, but there's nothing external.

You can decide, 'I'm going to make this film' or 'I'm not going to make this film.' "

In contrast, when Meyer was going through the 1991 reverse merger with Samuel Goldwyn, he admits he felt the stress. "Part of the stress is that you are dealing with external factors and they aren't moving at the pace you want," he says. "You can't *make* things happen. You end up spending a great deal of your time pushing and shoving, and some of that creates pressures and frustrations."

We'll talk more about the importance of clearly identifying your stress factors as controllable or uncontrollable a little later.

PSYCHOLOGICAL — Are You at the Mercy of Your Childhood?

Psychological influences include the mental and emotional components that constitute your personality. Some personality characteristics are innate, as mentioned, and some are a result of childhood influences, which will be discussed later. The point is, your relationships with family, friends, coworkers, and the world, whether stressful or unstressful, are based on the psychological and behavioral factors that comprise your personality.

Many personality traits can affect your stress levels, including chronic worrying, poor communication, low self-esteem, nonassertiveness, and suppressed anger. The pattern, of course, tends to be cyclical as these traits lead to stress (and diseases, as mentioned), which reinforces these traits, which leads to more stress, ad infinitum. Unfortunately the cycle often expands to include more overt behavior such as alcoholism and criminal acts.

I'm going to take a look at a few personality traits so that you can see how deeply they affect your level of stress and thus your life. The good news is that when weaker psychological traits are strengthened, your world can be transformed. People too often spend their energies focusing outward, trying to alter the outside world when the more effective approach is from inside. I'll talk later about how to work with these traits so they need no longer be hinderances.

Are you a worrier? The answer is most probably "yes," according to statistics. Psychology professor Thomas Borkovec, Ph.D., Pennsylvania State University, says only 30 percent of the population can be considered nonworriers, which means they worry less than an hour and a half a day and don't consider worrying a problem. The majority of us worry from 10 to 50 percent of the waking hours of each day!

Worry is one way we attempt to handle our "uncontrollables," yet ironically it most often results in even more psychological turmoil and stress. Worry can make you sick physically as well as mentally. As many as two-thirds of all people who visit a doctor are the "worried well," people who experience emotional problems as physical problems.

Sunkist CEO Russ Hanlin seldom worries. In fact, he says he's not really sure what stress is. Russ explains, "I've always felt that I have worked to do the best I can, and so I never really went home at night—even when the most serious problems were in evidence—and felt stress. I could always sleep at night."

One client laughed when she told me how she completely panicked just before delivering an important speech. She had given the same speech perhaps 50 times before but because this was a particularly significant event, she worried for weeks in advance and "lost it" when she heard her name introduced. Fortunately, she was able to get herself on stage with frozen smile intact; and because the speech was so familiar, her "automatic pilot" kicked in to get her through the first five minutes. After that she relaxed a bit and somehow made it to the end, her dignity undamaged. Nobody ever knew of the internal stress that had waged beneath her composed smile. She laughed in the aftermath, realizing she had unnecessarily created her own monster. A mind monster, left unchecked, that became very real.

Many of us do the same thing. For example, one night I knew I would be taking my pet rabbit Lassiter to the doctor the following morning for neutering. I worried myself into quite a state, imagining what that poor bunny would go through. In the midst of my negative visualizing, I looked down at him peacefully cleaning himself after his dinner. I realized that because he was unaware of the upcoming trauma, he was spending no energy worrying about it; he was anxiety free. I, however, had lived through the scene at least 10 times, letting my mind take me to a state of butterflies-in-the-stomach stress. After the deed was done, I recognized the folly of my worry. The outcome would be the same either way. All the energy I used for worrying was completely useless.

Are you angry? Therapists estimate that about half of their patients come to them for help in expressing anger. Repressed anger is said to significantly affect our level of stress and consequently our health. Repression makes one feel frustrated and out of control.

Anger and accompanying emotions like guilt and depression can be thought of as energy that, when trapped in the body as stress, turns inward to conditions like asthma, migraines, and rheumatoid arthritis, which as previously mentioned, are common physical manifestations of stress.

I have had many clients who disclaim anger as if it's something to be ashamed of. "I'm not mad about anything," they defend, upon my suggestion that we do an anger-releasing exercise together. (They often have a distorted view of anger and what they should do with it.) Interestingly, these same people may be chronic overeaters or admit to frequent episodes of depression, which are considered common by-products of suppressed anger. Depression is quite common in our society, although not exactly cocktail party conversation material. According to the American Psychological Association, Americans average at least two clinically diagnosable episodes of depression between ages 35 and 65. Not surprisingly, when anger is released, so is depression in many cases.

You are what you were: your childhood. In getting to know stress we must not forget to consider the cause of the personality traits discussed above. Old definitions don't look at the deeper roots of stress. Why do you tend to suppress anger? Or, why do you worry excessively? Most often because of early unresolved stress experiences in life; traumas of our childhood that are carried into adulthood in the form of debilitating traits including anger, low self-esteem, and depression. These defensive traits are integrated into your adult personality and affect the way you act and react, the way you adapt to stress. Different childhood experiences result in different adult responses to the same stressor.

Augie Nieto thinks many successful people have had to overcome childhood adversity in their lives, such as dealing with an alcoholic or inattentive parent. They then spend their entire lives trying to make themselves unique and special—something they were not as children. Augie admits, "As a child, I wasn't really recognized. With five kids vying for attention, you try to be unique." He continues, "Until recently, I never did things unless I got credit for them. I never did them for personal satisfaction. That's the big change."

Children are often taught that negative emotions are taboo, especially for little people. Unexpressed, these feelings have nowhere to go and often come out in the form of compulsions and fears. Unresolved, they are exaggerated and carried into adulthood. Later in life, if unresolved, one establishes a compensatory pattern such as passive-aggressiveness in place of expressing negative emotions. And we wonder what went wrong as we sign the divorce papers....

Recognition of early stress is a healthy first step. You can then direct the psychological skills described in Part II toward yourself as an adult as well as toward that child and other subselves inside who are still carrying around harmful personality traits. You may find it helpful to read more research about the inner child from experts like John Bradshaw. You may also choose to get some guidance from an experienced therapist.

PARADIGMS Are You at the Mercy of Your World-View?

> *"We are all captives of the pictures in our heads—our belief that the world we experience is the world that really exists."*
>
> *—Walter Lippmann*

All the factors that shape your stress—psychological, environmental, and genetic—together form your perception of the world, your reality, your paradigm.

How to Redefine Your Stress Reality. You've heard the expression "you are what you eat." In regard to stress, I often say, "you are what you think." And your thinking, as we've discussed, is based on your genetic, environmental, and psychological background. But you don't have to be captive to your thoughts. If you can change your perception of the world (including stress), you can change your state of stress.

Paradigm examination is one of the most interesting areas to explore in conquering stress. This goes beyond slapping on new positive thinking maxims. It means challenging your ideologies, your reality. Some ideologies are embedded pretty deeply, others are not. For example, John Bargh, New York University psychologist, believes we don't usually exercise control over automatic, unconscious influences on behavior and judgment. Beliefs, he says, can be born just by passive acceptance of "unedited incoming information." So eventually, we have adopted an unchallenged idea about something. For example, we have an idea about what causes us stress that may very well be embedded by erroneous information.

The trouble with "incoming information" is that it doesn't usually breeze in the ears and breeze out the mouth. It hangs around and proliferates. Experts say we have about 60,000 thoughts a day and that 90 percent of them are the same ones we had yesterday! This means we keep reinforcing our world-view with the same patterns of memory, which then help decide what new ones (or shall I say versions of the old ones) we will accept next. In this sense, we are prisoners of our own thought structure, of our own little imperfect version of reality upon which we base all our actions.

This reality is etched into our brains, quite literally, in the form of neural connections (nerve routes) that work almost like mini freeways, patterned and modified by environmental stimulation and experience. Repeated experience establishes its own route and its own response in our brain. Unfortunately, this route is too often malformed so that if we are bitten by a dog, for example, we build a crooked neural freeway that tells us all dogs are to be feared forever. And we go through life with layers and layers of erroneous neural freeways—erroneous perceptions such as this.

This "experience forms perceptions" idea was the subject of an experiment at Stanford University that raised two sets of kittens in two different worlds of perception. One group of kittens was raised with only horizontal figures and stripes; the other group saw only vertical stripes. When introduced later in life to the opposite stripes, neither group could even see them (i.e. the horizontal-raised kittens did not recognize the vertical lines and vice versa). The only thing they acknowledged was what they had experienced; what they knew. The conclusion of the study was that our experience shapes our perception. The opposite also appears to be true: perception shapes our experience. The way we think about something based, perhaps, on things we've read or heard (rather than experienced) determines how we will react to them in the future.

A famous Massachusetts Institute of Technology (MIT) paper on the study of perception, titled "What the Frog's Eye Tells the Frog's Brain," concludes, in essence, that a frog does not see what we see. We buy dog food based on *our* perceptions of that food, not our pets' perceptions. (Dogs don't care how "deep meaty red" it looks; they are color blind, for the most part.) Similarly, although you are the same species as your neighbor, you do not see, hear, or believe the same things. She is a Catholic, loves jazz and the color blue. You, a blue-hating Protestant raised on classical music, can't relate or (more accurately) can't perceive her personal reality, her paradigm. You can't see her horizontal stripes just as she most probably cannot see your vertical stripes.

Here's a fun little paradigm test you can do yourself if you have access to a video camera. Have someone tape you playing a sport you think you're pretty good at, like tennis or golf. There you are, the next Jimmy Conners, keeping your eye on the ball, staying down, following through, and smacking that ball. Now, look at the video. There you are in living color, up on your tip-toes, eye on the opponent, and using the racquet like a fly swatter—not exactly a Jimmy look-alike. The experience is humbling, educational, but most importantly, paradigm expanding.

We cling to our own self-built reality because, introspection aside, it is the only thing we have. Who are you to yourself if not your ideas? It can be quite alarming to see our reality crumble before our eyes, so we cling to what we know and reinforce it in any way possible. Our individualized reality provides a seemingly solid foundation that is, on the surface, predictable and tangible.

Our paradigms promise to protect us but, in fact, impose limitations on our life experience. Instead of a full global experience, we base our existence on a room without a view.

"But what if I'm perfectly happy in my room?" you ask. "Why should I change?" Let's not forget our mission here: to conquer stress. If you can learn to expand your limited reality, you can apply that skill to alter your ingrained definition and experience of stress. If your views are limited or erroneous, they may be neutral, but are more likely harmful, to one degree or another. In fact, most problems can be traced to our fixed and limited image of self and the world; our identification with false paradigms. (Politics are one example of this, but let's not get distracted.)

As we discussed, our thoughts are translated to our bodies, which affects us for better or worse, sooner or later. A Chinese acupuncturist once told me to soften my knees and be more fluid in my movements. "Westerners are too rigid in their thinking and their bodies," she scolded, "and that leads to mental and physical sickness." (When you think of the maze of billboards and other media influences that tell us what we should think, do, wear, eat, smell like, and be, you begin to realize the extent to which our culture reinforces rigid, unconscious paradigms.)

I have a client who is just discovering the influence her gone-but-not-forgotten mother had on her. Because she was sickly as a child, her mother was overprotective. She made her drink orange juice before getting out of bed every morning, whether or not she was sick. Today she not only refuses to drink orange juice but, still affected by those overpowering "sick" horizontal stripes, is chronically sick.

"He wouldn't let me breathe," another client blurted out one day in relating a story about her father. I asked if she thought this might be related to her ongoing asthma. She stopped cold. "Absolutely," she admitted, half shocked.

Another client had an overbearing mother about whom I was one day inquiring. I asked if he had ever spoken back to his mother. "Occasionally," he said, "when she really got to me I would finally yell, 'Get off my back!' " This was the piece of the puzzle I had been looking for, and I asked, "Do you think this might have any connection with your chronic back problems?" He looked at the ground for a long time, finally nodding. Old paradigms trapped in your body take their toll. Don't brush off every ailment or injury as an accident, genetic, or otherwise. Ask your deeper self the true source. Then bend those paradigms as the answer arises.

How to challenge your paradigm. Why should you challenge your paradigms? Because it's good for you. It takes a lot of energy to maintain a false reality, and since you know about adaptation energy, you know you can't afford to squander it.

How do you change your ideas and values? Some can be changed just by challenging them, others need more work. But first, you need to acknowledge that your paradigm imposes limitations. If you think about it, you may have already caught glimpses of your true self out of the corner of your paradigm-eye, as you really are. We generally choose to dive back under our blankets of perception rather than look any closer. But if we can stay above the blankets long enough to get through the initial discomfort, we'd witness the excitement of broader vision—full sunlight and an expanded world—and we would never go back under again. Above the blankets you can redefine your whole reality: success and failure, happiness and suffering, health and sickness, and yes, stress and tranquility.

The next time you hear yourself righteously defending or criticizing an ideology, stop and try to step out of yourself for a minute. Play a little game with yourself, ask: Where did I pick this up? Why do I believe this? Be willing and ready to have your ideas modified or even completely obliterated by new information. Think in terms of looking forward to the opportunity of changing your opinion about things rather than clinging tightly to familiar old ideas, your sense of identity, your ego.

Practice expanding your ego-supported paradigm by saying, "That's an interesting point of view. You may be right." At first, it's almost a little scary when you let go of your paradigm security blanket. You hang suspended in midbelief as you consider another point of view. Like a monkey looking for the next vine to grab in his flight through the air, we want to hold some point of view. I know some people who never change their positions (or at least never admit to it), and others who swing without warning, almost violently, to another equally limited perspective.

Grab another vine once in a while, or better, try hanging in midbelief. Consider the notion that nothing is solidly wedged in permanency. With friends I occasionally switch paradigms midstream: "Athletes and actors get paid too much because..." Then, "They don't get paid enough because..." I find this an expanding and entertaining exercise.

Think of our children being raised in horizontal- or vertical-indoctrined households. Think of this the next time you have trouble understanding someone else's point of view. Even if you can't recreate other people's reality in your mind, at least be aware that their reality *is* perfectly logical, as logical as yours is to you. If you are really having a difficult time feeling compassion for someone, make up a story that might account for that particular person's behavior or perspective: "She could have been ridiculed as a child because she was overweight, and thus has a defensive chip on her shoulder today." With compassion and understanding comes less stress.

Before blindly reacting to old stressors, try to examine the root paradigm that is responsible for your reaction. "This deadline is impossible" becomes "Just because my mother did her Christmas shopping in August doesn't mean that I have to take on her everything-gets-done-in-advance paradigm and choke over this demanding but reasonable work assignment." Decide how to modify your beliefs and restructure your approach. Expand your paradigm and make it more flexible, but also remember that expanded or not, yours is not the only paradigm in town. Have compassion for the perspectives of others. In working toward a flexible, global perspective versus a limited singular one, you will get a little closer to your true nature and the world around you.

Paradigm Wrap-Up:

1. Examine the paradigms that sustain your stress.
2. Practice challenging and expanding your paradigm (thoughts, opinions, ideologies) on a daily basis.
3. Accept that others have their own well-founded paradigm that is just as legitimate as yours, right or wrong.

CHAPTER 4

HARD WORK NEVER KILLED ANYBODY—BUT STRESS HAS

"In a company, a person feels like an oarsman. The boat's going through the water—are you pulling in unison and are you pulling hard enough?"

—Augie Nieto, CEO, Life Fitness

If we can minimize the degree of stress we experience from our jobs, we should be about halfway to conquering stress, since work (and commuting) consumes roughly half of our waking hours. And since the workplace represents the rest of our world, our workplace stress skills will apply to the other parts of our lives.

IS STRESS A NECESSARY EVIL ON THE ROAD TO SUCCESS?

Job stress should not be taken lightly or numbed with a glass of wine or even exercise. Since it represents one-half of your life and deeply affects the other half, it should be contemplated and treated seriously.

Seven out of ten of us who work have significant job stress—significant in that we're not just talking about it, we're visiting doctors. Unfortunately, the situation is not getting any better. Worker's compensation claims related to stress have tripled since 1980. The loss to our economy is estimated as high as $150 billion per year and rising. These claims even threaten to bankrupt the system in some states. The bottom line is that stress is getting worse. Why?

There is a breed of stressors unique to the modern business arena, including hostile takeovers, ever-increasing mergers and acquisitions, as well as environmental conditions and commuting difficulties. We even have fancy new names for our stressors, like *technostress*. Technostress is used to describe the stress brought on by our high-tech work environment, which includes minutia such as computer key-strokes per minute counts and monitored rest-room breaks.

Another all-too-common source of stress is that which we put on ourselves. Samuel Goldwyn's Meyer Gottlieb says, "The most heartfelt stress is the stress I put on myself, which is based on my own expectations and to what extent I achieve those." If we continually set goals that are too high, we can put ourselves in the long-term, no-win stress category. Meyer doesn't have this problem. He says, "I achieve my goals most of the time. I don't set goals that are too high."

Information overload is another rather self-explanatory term resulting from our over-accelerated pace of data acquisition and communication enhancements, like fax machines, cellular phones, computers, and beepers. An obvious irony to me is that in spite of our ever-burgeoning developments in communication, one of the biggest problems we have in regard to stress is *communication* (which will be discussed later).

DOES YOUR JOB MAKE YOU SICK?

"Stress is fear of the unknown."
—Augie Nieto, CEO, Life Fitness

Not surprisingly, job satisfaction is a major factor in longevity. If you enjoy what you do and work conditions are good, you stand a much better chance of living longer. This holds for women as well as men and raises some interesting questions regarding women's work or stay-at-home dilemma. A study done by epidemiologist Donna Kritz-Silverstein at the University of California School of Medicine found that women who worked were less prone to heart attacks than those who didn't. They had lower blood pressure, cholesterol, blood sugar, and other predictors of heart disease. The thing to note is that the women studied were in upwardly mobile jobs. It was thought that these women feel more control over their lives, and thus are happier and under less stress than women who stay at home. Kritz-Silverstein says that the findings may not hold for women in less challenging jobs. She thinks it may only be healthier for women to be employed if they enjoy what they are doing.

Unfortunately, most of us do not enjoy what we do; and it's no wonder. Jobs have ambiguity, uncertainty, poor relations with coworkers, boredom, and lack of recognition in abundance, so say statistics. An undesirable workplace atmosphere, of course, leads to stress and bad health, which can mean higher cholesterol, alcoholism, psychiatric illness, gastrointestinal problems, smoking, high blood pressure, and cardiovascular disease.

In regard to job ambiguity, Augie Nieto says, "If you know where you're going there's nothing to be worried about. You can always do the job, but the toughest thing is not knowing what the job is." An astute, caring boss, Augie continues, "The better you can define what their job is, the more employees are aware of what's expected of them, the less stress they will have, and the better performers they will be." Augie feels the worst stress people have to deal with is peer pressure: "What do people think of me? Am I doing my job and pulling my weight?"

Some stress studies have shown that the most stressed workers are in middle management and below. This may be over simplified to some degree, and it probably depends on individual factors and personality traits as much as type of job.

And certainly, as I found in my study of America's top CEOs, upper management executives have their own brand of stress. Although they don't always call it stress, the CEOs I interviewed for this book, similar to heads of other corporations, work intensely and often more than 40 hours a week. In addition, there are "save the ship" and "sell the ship" type stresses that plague these leaders.

Meyer Gottlieb of Samuel Goldwyn had a roller-coaster 1991 when Samuel Goldwyn went public. They did a reverse merger, parting from their parent company. Meyer says, "A lot of energy went into that transaction. We thought it was going to be a six-month deal and it turned out to be a twelve-month deal. There was a lot of stress associated with that."

While continuing to head Life Fitness, Augie Nieto sold it to Balley's in 1984. Then in July 1991 he bought it back. He admitted it was, "pretty stressful." He said, "It goes back to uncertainty. It was announced we were being sold, then there was the Persian Gulf War. There was a recession and there wasn't a bank that wanted to lend money to an industry they thought was a fad." Augie made 17 bank presentations in nine months and finally came up with the ideal buyer who invested 45 percent equity and believed in what the company was going to do. A happy ending but another roller-coaster stress ride.

In any case, whether you run a corporation or not, it may be no surprise to learn that the same methods that improve stress will also boost the corporation's productivity. While boosting corporate productivity is not the focus of this book, I mention it as yet another reason to take a serious look at stress. Be informed and maintain a realistic bird's eye view of the stress you are subjected to in your career.

All jobs do not have the same stress potential. Different characteristics define a job's level of stress, such as control and demand as well as good or bad bosses and environment. You should also be aware that there are different stressors at different stages of your career.

Early career stressors often revolve around being under or over promoted. Mid-career stressors are a bit more complex. There is usually an increase in dependency on specialists that you often don't fully understand. Expectations and competition increase, which commonly limits camaraderie.

BAD BOSS ALERT

Whether you are the boss or the bossed, we are all bossed by something or somebody. Everybody's got to serve somebody, to paraphrase Bob Dylan. However, it's important to recognize the qualities of a bad boss so that you know you're not the one who's out of line when conflicts occur.

When you have a bad boss, it is a common but unhealthy mentality to grin and bear your job until 5 P.M. each day. Depression, insomnia, and feelings of dread or panic often result. How do you know if it's you or your boss? For starters, a bad boss usually offers little support and instills a feeling of low self-worth (that "Gee, I guess I'm just lucky to have any job at all" guilt-tinged feeling). A boss's unpredictability and expectations that change from day to day are other qualities that will keep you on edge. A boss that constantly sets up win/lose work goals is another bad sign. Is your work judged in very black and white ways? It's either good or bad with no in-between? Loss of creative input or freedom in a job is another red flag. Studies show that if a boss increases the demands on workers but limits their freedom to make decisions, employees commonly experience raised blood pressure. Other symptoms of work overload or stress that you should know about, as mentioned previously, include:

- Elevated cholesterol
- Insomnia
- Boredom

- Alcoholism
- Gastrointestinal problems
- Psychiatric illness
- Smoking
- Job accidents
- Poor performance

A good boss should be as aware of not being overly demanding as of demanding too little. Some of you may think that a low-demand job sounds like a job made in heaven. Think again. A job that is too easy for you can be as stressful as a job that is too demanding. Besides causing stress, depression, anxiety, and apathy, a job that is too easy can lead to skill atrophy and negative growth. Sound like an exciting way to spend half of your life?

Bad Boss Alert Summary

Watch for any of these signs: Your boss

- limits your freedom and input.
- offers little support.
- is consistently unpredictable.
- makes excessive physical demands.
- makes excessive psychological demands.

WHY YOU SHOULD MATCH YOUR PERSONALITY WITH THE RIGHT COMPANY

Just as bosses have their own personalities, so do entire companies. Try to match your personality to the company. It is no accident that Russ Hanlin stayed with Sunkist for 42 years. Russ came to Sunkist when he was just 18 and got drafted one year later. To his surprise and delight, Sunkist had a military leave of absense program and they arranged a work program so Russ could go to college at the same time. After school Russ returned full time to Sunkist and has worked hard for them ever since. Russ laughs humbly as he says, "I would like to think they were compensated for their generosity." While Russ had other offers, many of them seemingly better than his position at Sunkist, during the 42 years, he stayed with the corporate personality he liked.

Another personality attraction of the Russ-Sunkist marriage: Russ is a Type A personality and Sunkist is a Type A company. There is a great urgency that is inherent in a company that deals with highly perishable products, according to Russ. While this would create a lot of stress for many people, Russ loves it. "I'm very much excited by what we do here—the importance of it and the urgency of it."

Russ says that because of the "rush-rush" nature of the business, more than $800 million of their business is conducted on good faith, without one thing written on a piece of paper. There simply isn't time for contracts, signatures, and a lot of discussion. Just reading this may make some of you nervous, but it may stimulate others. How did you react? How much of a challenge are you comfortable with?

Analyze a company just as they do you before accepting a job. Some companies are definitely more balanced and well structured than others. Psychosocial work characteristics should correlate with every part of your makeup—your values, skills, perception, physiological functioning—as much as possible.

What if circumstances don't allow you the perfect job, even though you may know what to look for? First of all, remember that just *recognizing* that you are exposed to certain job stresses is a valuable antistressor. It is reassuring to be clear that the problem is not of your own making, and that it is not something you have to internalize.

Second, if temporarily situated in an unsatisfying job, learn to apply the appropriate Stress-Conquering skills, as described later, such as imagining a protective boundary around yourself.

MUST A WORK CRISIS CAUSE A PERSONAL CRISIS?

Tainted hierarchy such as a bad boss is an ongoing and always erosive source of stress, but a corporate crisis refers to the-ship's-in-danger-of-going-down state of affairs, and is usually a more immediate and dramatic source of stress. But must a crisis at work mean a crisis for you?

While entire books have been written on business crisis, my intent here is to help you realize some of the key points about stress and job crises. Crisis in business is not too different from crisis in real life. Gerald Meyers, author of *When It Hits the Fan*, found that crisis in a business affects people much the same as Elisabeth Kubler-Ross's stages of impending death. The problem is that most businesses are reluctant to plan for adversity, and consequently, when it hits, everyone in the company is affected. Deny potential disaster and maybe it will go away. Success is emphasized in most companies, not potential failure.

If a crisis is detected early and aggressively managed all the way, damage can be minimized considerably, and stress can be reduced both on corporate and individual levels. Meyer Gottlieb of Samuel Goldwyn says that when a certain department has a crisis, he tries to act as a stabilizing force. "I try to be calm when they're not," he says. "That's my role and it's something I pay a great deal of attention to." When Meyer needs a break from the "stream of pressures" in his office, he walks around and jokes with some of the people on the floor. "I'll do some comedy, something crazy, and just get some fun in it." He reduces his stress by reducing theirs! And his employees like it. Meyer says, "I have an open door policy and the employees make good use of it." Augie of Life Fitness and Russ of Sunkist have similar policies.

Aside from selecting a compassionate boss, what else can you do to decrease your stress reaction to a company crisis? Being informed is a good start. When a crisis climaxes, whether personal or corporate, you must first fully understand the problem. You should then consider the choices available and share them with a superior or friend, whatever the case. Then, to the extent that you can, you need to move toward a solution, again with the help of a superior, if necessary. Finally, you must try to eliminate the cause of the crisis where possible so it doesn't happen again.

One high-powered Wall Street stock exchange executive told me that during a crisis he always sleeps with a pad and phone by his head because he receives so many emergency calls at all hours from all over the world. As an aside, he mentioned that certain countries always panic faster than others when times get tough. If there is a genetic factor to stress, could there also be stress-sensitivity common denominators among nationalities?

Another executive told me that several employees—about 20 percent of lower-level staff—panicked and quit during one particularly bad crisis. While that didn't exactly boost company morale, he said it worked out because it saved him the job of firing them. According to this executive, coolness amidst a storm is not easily learned. "You've gotta' go with what you've got, and even that gets pushed to the limits," he said. Negative attitudes within the ranks cannot usually be changed overnight, but it is common practice to instruct staff to restrict their fear and pessimism to the offices of their superiors.

Certain people can never be relied upon to be positive factors in a crisis, but these otherwise valuable people can often be contained, thus avoiding the contagious transfer of stress inside and outside corporate walls. One CEO once overhead a junior staffer inappropriately exposing his panic to his peers in a time of crisis, saying, "We're finished." In the end, the company wasn't finished, but the junior staffer was. This CEO told me that in times of crisis, upper management is often told not to come in to work if they feel they can't maintain an optimistic attitude on a given day.

High level managers must keep morale up within the company while being honest with the employees. They must also show a positive attitude to the outside world. Upper level managers often have public relations responsibilities and must say the right thing at the right time, so that any internal confusion or panic doesn't spread to the rest of the world, thus creating an even worse negative feedback loop. The release of information must be controlled and carefully planned. And finally, this same executive must stay internally motivated, positive, and strong.

How do they keep themselves protected? Each has a unique formula, but my Wall Street executive said he learned to cut himself off after work and go for a run to be alone rather than hanging out socially with his co-workers. He created his own protective shell and revitalized himself for the next day. Does stress ever affect these executives? One admitted, "Of course you feel it. But you don't really know how it's affecting you, what damage is actually being done."

CRISIS PRESENTS OPPORTUNITY

This maxim used to irritate me. Someone's over-optimistic, Pollyanna slant on a just-plain-bad situation. But time and experience brought me to see the wisdom of this phrase. Can good come from a crisis? Yes. The head of Sunkist admitted that he discovered a lot of superfluous jobs during their crisis that he still hasn't replaced, even though they are back in full operation. Others agreed.

Another positive aspect to the Sunkist crisis, according to Russ, was that "everyone kind of pulled together." He said that in a situation where nobody's to blame, "There's almost a camaraderie that comes out of it in surviving."

Crisis also forces a corporation to face latent problems and accelerate changes that are perhaps long overdue. New strategies and early warning systems are often developed that make a company smarter and tougher in the long run.

When those in the corporation are educated and updated, even though the information may change daily, stress is diminished, morale is boosted, and companies are saved. If people are not kept informed, the symptoms of crisis are manifested, such as panic, anger, and denial. Most everyone I interviewed agreed that many crises cannot be completely circumvented, so be prepared: View a crisis as an opportunity to learn and grow both internally and externally.

PART II: MAKING FRIENDS WITH THE ENEMY: THE SOLUTION TO STRESS

CHAPTER 5

THE PLAN OF ATTACK

"Stress doesn't exist—it's a product of the intellect."

We know that there is no standard solution to stress. Conquering stress requires that we look at interconnections of the body and mind as well as the world and self; it requires a systems approach as opposed to a linear one. It also requires that we change our attitudes as well as our habits. This is new to us because we are accustomed to quick fixes and medicinal cures, so that we can get on with the busy-ness that fills our lives.

Since much modern day stress originates in the brain, it is interesting and apropos to take a brief look at how the brain works. In its balanced state, the brain works in a systems way. Scientists used to be proud of the fact that they dissected the brain down to individual neuron activities—one neuron does this, another does that. But they now recognize the significance of looking at the brain on a broader scale, as a "systems" organ. Like ants working for a common purpose of the colony, so do our neurons, in simultaneous neuron "computations." The capabilities of the brain, in this sense, extend far beyond the capabilities of any computer. So, beginning with the brain itself, we must look at the solution to stress with an expanded, whole systems perspective.

According to mind-body expert Deepak Chopra, M.D., our brains' thoughts extend throughout our bodies. We have a "thinking body," says Chopra. Stressful thoughts permeate our body and thus must be handled in a whole system/whole person way. Thus, the term *wholistic*. We must become familiar with the connection between thoughts, behavior, and automatic neurophysiological function, as discussed in Part I.

While there are standard aspects that should be addressed in the process of befriending stress, the approach should take into account the whole person, and should be customized according to individual needs. There is no magic trick or pill that will take your troubles away, but there are four very effective steps that will give you a greater knowledge of self in the process of conquering stress.

STEP ONE Take Active Responsibility for Your Stress Recovery

The decision itself to take responsibility for your stress can make a significant difference in your level of stress. A strong conviction that you can and will make a change, versus passive acceptance of a negative situation, is your best ally, and without it the other steps will not happen.

Taking responsibility is different from merely acknowledging that you are responsible. We can know that we are fully responsible but that responsibility can ferment to guilt as we sit in front of the TV day after day. Being active, however, means that changes will take place.

Conquering stress depends on how diligently you practice some fairly simple skills. Internal skills such as those needed to eliminate stress require practice just like any other skill from chess to dancing. Why should we need skills to relax? Why not just get out the golf clubs or turn on the television? Golf, television, shopping, and gardening may offer a great escape and temporary relaxation, but they do not eliminate the anxiety or neurophysiological response of prolonged stress. Internal skills are required for this—it is one thing a doctor can't do for you.

The fact that stress has become so prevalent in our country is unfortunate, but it is an ideal crisis-creates-opportunity chance to look within and become familiar with that person our legs have been carrying around all these years. It is the initial "be responsibile" part that is perhaps the toughest for many. Once results are felt, however, the momentum picks up along with the desire.

And what is our motivation for reducing our level of stress? The answer isn't as obvious as it might seem. As a HealthStyle motivation consultant, I find it challenging enough to encourage people to exercise, eat right, and lose weight—even when there is a big element of vanity and a visual reward in store. In contrast, stress-related aches and pains are often perceived as macho, proof, somehow, of our heroic efforts at work, for example.

Being stressed, like being sick, serves a purpose (usually unconscious) for some people. To paraphrase the lyrics of a Carly Simon song: Suffering used to make me feel like I was alive. The reasons for choosing to suffer can run deep and some may require professional help to overcome them. Fortunately, many people are now seeking recovery from stress. Their motivation to take such action, I have found, is a matter of the pain-comfort ratio.

People usually seek relief when the pain of the problem outweighs the pain (or effort) of the cure, or what is perceived as such. In some cases the effort is significant and beyond the scope of what many are willing to do. Most of the time the imagined effort to change is often worse than the actual effort required.

There is also a great deal of people who will suffer long after the ratio for change has passed. Remember that only 15 to 20 percent of patients take an active role in their own education and recovery. (This has to do with the psychological factors, like feeling unworthy and suffering low self-esteem, which will be discussed later.) My hope is that people start taking responsibility much earlier, before their bodies demand action by screaming out through one ailment or another.

The good news about taking active responsibility and learning new things is that you grow and gain a heightened knowledge of who you are. It is easy to never really get close to our deeper selves in this rush of doing (versus living) life, but when we are faced with something like having to deal with stress, we can come out with a whole lot more: a new, redefined sense of self and a new enemy-turned-friend—stress.

STEP TWO Identify Your Stressors and Your Mind-Body Responses to Them

We let stressors run rampant in our heads, skittering here and there, butting their noses into every thought we have. By identifying them, we have at least corralled them to some extent—an important step. A study on witch doctors and psychiatrists demonstrated that patients felt better after visits with each because, among other reasons, each authority figure exuded certainty (accompanied by a fancy headress, diploma, etc.) and had also given their condition a name. They no longer had a scary, elusive illness but a known and therefore a conceivably controllable thing. The same applies to stress.

If we can give the authority headress or diploma to ourselves and name our stressors, we can diffuse it by "knowing it to death."

Once you've identified your stressors, you can learn to pay attention to your particular early warning signs of stress, physical as well as psychological, as described in Part I. With practice, you will skillfully be able to recognize stress in its premature stage and take appropriate early action.

You are not your stressors. Much stress management advice puts misplaced emphasis on learning to avoid what stresses us. This approach can cause problems such as reinforcing and further embedding old stressors in our consciousness. The Holmes and Rahe Stress Scale I mentioned earlier is educational to some degree, but it can also implant a preconceived incorrect notion of stress. We must guard against preprogrammed stress from within and without.

I met a distinguished older man in an exclusive neighborhood the week before Christmas who told me that he couldn't visit his nearby son on Christmas. I asked him why, and he kind of laughed while shrugging his shoulders. He said that his wife didn't like busy freeways. Seeing sadness behind his smile I enthusiastically reminded him that the freeways aren't busy on Christmas Day. He shook his head and chuckled again in a resigned way, and said, "I know, but she still doesn't like them." This woman had programmed herself on one perhaps unpleasant freeway trip and hasn't questioned her programming since. She just got it in her head that she didn't like freeways, and it will continue to control both of their lives until they die.

Another example: I have a friend who loved bike riding. It took away his troubles and left him with a feeling of well-being. He rode every day and twice a day whenever possible. He was hooked. Then it happened. One day he "almost got hit by a car," was traumatized, and hasn't been on a bike since. I suppose his thinking goes something like, "Better off stressed than dead." Stuck erroneous programming.

By thinking only one way about a certain circumstance ("This is a stressful situation and always has been"), we can't learn or grow much. Migraines, for example, are exacerbated by fearing the oncoming headache—sort of a conditioned response. My message is to *un*condition, to desensitize those responses instead of dodging a preprogrammed event for an entire lifetime. This desensitization is accomplished, in part, by identifying that which caused your stress. *We must identify our stressors, not identify with them.*

Take a moment now to list your stressors:

1.
2.
3.
4.

Then look at that list and see those stressors as separate from you. *You are not your stressors.*

Challenging your perception, your world-view, is another part of this process and will be discussed later.

How to Identify Your Physical Responses to Stress and Free up Your Energy

"The years go by and life rolls on,
We all search for the reasons why.
When times get hard we could use a good laugh,
Sometimes we could use a good cry.
There's really nothing to hide,
Don't let your emotions get locked up inside.
Let it go. Let it go.
Let the spirit move the soul."

—Jeff Harrington

Where do you feel stress in your body? We never really think too much about it, but most of us can locate it in our bodies if we just stop and concentrate for a moment.

Think of your body as a flowing stream of energy. Now imagine boulders blocking that stream at various parts of your body. Stress acts like those boulders, blocking vital energy flow thoughout your body. When you get home from a stressful day at work, you feel exhausted. This exhaustion is not because you are so physically or even mentally taxed but rather because you have developed emotion-induced, energy-blocking boulders throughout your lifeforce energy system. If unaltered, these boundaries can devastate your state of mind, goals, and life. Incidently, exercise advocates know that these boulders aren't physical exhaustion because once they exercise, they feel energized and alive again. Unfortunately however, most people haven't got the motivational skills to push themselves to even walk around the block, although they may know it reduces stress.

Try doing a boulder-removing, energy-recycling meditation as described in Stress-Conquering Skills (Chapter 7), and you will feel revived again and ready for exercise or anything else you want to do.

It's both fascinating and frightening to realize the damage that occurs from stress without our knowledge. It's also fascinating to realize that we can reverse this process just by being aware and redirecting negative energy. But if you don't know how to release and direct this energy, the results can be deadly. The Los Angeles riots spurred by the controversial Rodney King verdict in 1992 is a perfect example. Living in Los Angeles, I heard, saw, and felt the repercussions more "up close and personal" than I would have chosen. In attempting to console rioters and other angry citizens, I repeatedly heard city officials and religious leaders advise angry citizens to channel their energy into something useful, like voting on a certain proposition at a future date. Every time I heard these sincere but pitiful pleas, I felt their frustration. My reasons were many, but the most poignant was that most people don't know *how* to rechannel their energy. It is, for the most part, a meaningless concept. Energetic release in the form of property damage was an unsurprising outcome.

Unknowns and uncontrollables lead to negative emotional states, such as fear, frustration, depression, or anger, that cause physiological arousal. If left unreleased, this arousal turns to negative energy and can be harmful. As you may remember, Russ Hanlin of Sunkist has an abundance of energy, which he releases primarily in his work. But for 36 years he smoked 2 packs a day—one half million cigarettes. By his calculations, he put a cigarette to his mouth 500 times a day! This misplaced nervous energy could very easily have killed him.

STEP THREE Become "Stress Literate"

Stress is a left-brain disease. With some people, stress might be thought of as an imbalance of the left and right hemispheres of the brain—the analytical and the creative. (While this analogy is admittedly more anecodotal than scientific, it is useful for our purposes.) The left brain, the analytical mind, has taken over and is running the show. It is sending overload messages to the body, which in trying to help out, absorbs the strain. By learning to tune down the Analytical Mind and tune up the Creative ("Let's Party") Mind, something closer to balance is achieved. (The skills for conquering stress described later will help with this.)

What Is Control and Do You Have it?

"If there's a plan, well that's just fine,
But it's not under your control.
Everybody knows you can't hold back the wind,
So you might as well just let it go.
No matter which way you choose,
Sometimes you win and
Sometimes you lose..."

—*Jeff Harrington*

Whatever definitions have been given to stress, one word that continually pops up is *control*. If a person has little control over any aspect of his life, there is stress. Yes, I think one should be able to deal with uncontrollable situations in an unstressed manner, and I will tell you how. But we must also recognize the importance of establishing control in those areas of your life where possible.

Lack of control and its accompanying stress on the body is said to be a major source of risk for cardiovascular disease, more than the demanding load itself. A 1990 study by Cornell University Medical College was the first study to show a link between chronic job stress and hypertension. Specifically, it showed that those with little *control* over their jobs were three times as likely to develop hypertension (a leading cause of heart disease). Psychologists Suzanne C. Kobasa, Ph.D., and Salvatore Maddi, Ph.D., coined something called the "hardiness factor," which states that certain beliefs can make you more immune to stress and disease, such as a sense of control over your life.

Gaining control can be healthy and productive or it can be unhealthy and destructive. Gaining control is healthy and productive when you do it for the purpose of establishing order from chaos, when you assess the uncontrollables in your life and make the necessary changes where possible, such as organizational or time management improvements. In contrast, there are those who are "control freaks" in varying degrees. They are rigid and compulsive about control and are usually reacting from other causes. They want control for the sake of control, to boost their self-esteem, and give them a sense of power. Sunkist CEO Russ Hanlin talks about balance and control. While a part of him would like to handle everything, he knows he can't. "If there is a frustration in being a CEO, it is that you don't get to do anything yourself completely, from start to finish. The differentiation I've learned to make," he says, "is that I can *know* about everything, but I can't *do* everything. I can know enough to be confident in the decisions that are being made."

When you experience uncontrollables, do something that *is* in your control and rewarding, even if it's as simple as rearranging your closet or washing your car. Or, on a more growth-promoting level, learn to abide harmoniously with stress, using techniques such as vipassana meditation (see Chapter 9).

Clarify your comfort zone. Everyone has their own comfort zone regarding stress, and one should become familiar with the exact delineation of that zone. This delineation helps clarify and define what stress is to you. The balance is delicate: too much stimulation on one side, too little on the other is bad. To some extent, we unconsciously try to avoid input that is overwhelming, which is helpful. But by knowing your comfort zone parameter, you can then work to expand it (desensitization is discussed a little later), and thus gain some power and control while reducing your level of stress.

STEP FOUR Learn Stress-Conquering Skills

Stress-conquering skills will be described in detail. They include everything from changing your way of thinking about stress (redefining stress) to changing your physical and emotional experience of stress. Give yourself the option of accessing any and all possible skills for different circumstances. Some people adopt their favorites while others incorporate a complete arsenal of techniques.

A SUMMARY

FOUR STEPS TO NO (KNOW) STRESS

The steps to knowing stress are basic but effective.

1. Take responsiblity for your stress recovery. Make a stress-conquering plan that includes regular practice.
2. Identify your stressors. Also identify your body and mind responses to stress. Write them down.
3. Learn skills for conquering stress. Then learn to troubleshoot your self-identified stressors (in Step 2) with these skills, including internal and external skills (to follow).
4. Become educated, "stress literate." Among other things, understand the control issue: how to gain control as well as how to let go of it.

- Clarify your control comfort zones.
- Make logistical changes to modify or eliminate controllable stressors.
- Apply stress management skills to deal with uncontrollable stressors.

CHAPTER 6

HOW TO ACHIEVE "STRESS SUCCESS" IN YOUR JOB

"When work is souless, life stifles and dies."

—Albert Camus

One of the stronger messages from the study outlined in the book *Healthy, Wealthy & Wise* was that love, not money, drove America's top CEOs to these highest ranked positions. Almost one-half said that, other considerations aside, they would do what they do without pay.

Russ Hanlin has loved every job he's had at Sunkist over the past 42 years on his way to becoming CEO. "I've always worked at my job and enjoyed what I was doing and thought it was extremely important. I was absorbed in it," he says, adding with a laugh, "When a new opportunity came along I almost hated to leave the present job behind."

Sadly, it's been said that over 95 percent of us would not do what we are now doing for free. And, while we may all have a special vocational niche waiting somewhere for us, most of us never find it. So how can you be content in your work?

Examining and purifying your motives for your career goals is a good start. If career motives are based on position or money you will never feel fulfilled, even when your goals are. But in enjoying the challenge of your work instead of continually looking ahead, you show a better chance of finding contentment.

THE KEY: BALANCE

Loving what you do is important but so is balancing your work life and your home life. At times, this can be almost more difficult if you love your job than if you don't. Just ask the CEOs I talked with. Life Fitness CEO Augie Nieto struggled with this balance for years but finally got the message. He says one of the disadvantages of running a corporation is that "if you are successful or trying to be successful and you're growing, there are certain sacrifices to be made." Augie's sacrifice used to be spending little time with his family. In recent years he has concentrated on changing that. One particularly amusing story involves Augie's enthusiastic, polyphasic personality. Augie, a jock who has run in six marathons, decided he could spend time with his son and run a marathon at the same time. He pushed his then one-year-old son in a stroller the whole way. "He beat me by two feet," he says, laughing. Ah, the family that marathons together....

Gottlieb is also more aware of the need for balance these days, but admits it's a challenge. "You try to be fair to everyone [your business and your family]," he says. "Any way you go with your decision, you're not satisfying both sides 100 percent."

Sunkist's Russ Hanlin regrets that he didn't spend enough time with his kids when they were younger. He now has a more balanced view of his life and takes his wife with him when he travels. He says, "She's become a part of the business, in a sense, and plays an important part in the whole thing."

The business world and the imbalances it imposes on people's lives can be viewed as great opportunities for personal growth, much like other challenges in life, from running a marathon to conquering alcoholism to watching a loved one die of cancer. Remember the analogy of the work world as a microcosm of the larger world? At work, you have the opportunity each day to practice living, to turn stress into no-stress, to interact compassionately, to practice the art of life.

HOW TO CONQUER CAREER STRESS: CHANGE THE SYSTEM

Change is needed, but change in America's top corporations has been slow according to statistics. Productivity suffers along with workers' health, as I've stated. We need people trained to conquer stress on and off the job. We need to establish health monitoring feedback systems that individuals can do themselves, such as recording blood pressure, sleep patterns, and emotional states.

Workplace stress has too long been considered inevitable instead of preventable. Changes are needed within the corporate structure, including work reorganization. Some corporations are beginning to reevaluate assembly lines, for example, so that workers may feel a sense of self-accomplishment. In general, psychological and psychosocial aspects need special consideration. Other factors that need attention include:

1. Increase the control aspect of all jobs. Improved decision-making opportunities balance high demands.
2. Better defined job expectations and opportunity for advancement.
3. Honest and frequent communication between upper management and lower-level workers.
4. Challenge—the correct balance per individual need.
5. Recognition for job accomplishment. If necessary, ask your boss to do this; it increases your motivation to work. Suggest feedback or reward systems.
6. Eliminate uncertainty in all areas. Be informed, get educated when necessary, ask questions.

Russ Hanlin says that while the compensation is not terrific at Sunkist, there is "more longevity here than almost any other place you can go." He explains, "Employees understand how they fit in here and they have a respect for each other." He believes that with many companies a climate of uncertainty is typical and the employee "has no idea how his efforts contribute or if they're important or unimportant."

DOES YOUR JOB MOTIVATE YOU?

> *"To end up with a job that you really don't have the talent for has got to be really a debilitating thing."*
>
> *—Russ Hanlin, CEO, Sunkist*

Hans Selye believed in the work ethic. He said, "To achieve peace of mind and fulfillment through self-expression, most men need a commitment to work in the service of some cause that they can respect." According to Selye, the pursuit of pleasure alone cannot lead to true fulfillment. Nobel Prize laureate Albert Szent-Györgyi says, much the same: "Ability brings with it the need to use that ability."

Meyer Gottleib loves his job of running Samuel Goldwyn so much that he thinks of the company as his own. When he negotiates, Meyer says, "I often catch myself saying, 'You're asking me to spend *my* money!' " Augie Nieto's self-created business suits him perfectly. He says, "If you had a dream environment—to be an ex-jock and own an exercise business—it's pretty fun! It'd be like a football player being the general manager of a football team. I like it."

Great words. But I have a good friend who is a gifted musician, writer, and "media personality" who claims he has absolutely no desire to pursue these talents except for monetary reward. He opted instead to pursue his tennis and golf talents during a five-year hiatus. This brings us to the subject of motivation.

Understanding the concept of motivation helps clarify what your job should mean to you. Motivation keeps us vital, interested, and active. A motive is "some inner drive that causes a person to do something or act in a certain way; an incentive or goal," according to Webster's. Many think that everyone has creativity just waiting to be expressed. That may or may not be true, but I do know that if one's motivation is not strong enough, whatever creativity there is will stay dormant. Too many people put in their time at line-of-least-resistance jobs for which they are ill suited, while whatever creativity they may have is untapped.

While some personalities need to be encouraged to tap their talents, others need to maintain a realistic point of view. Some, for example, are convinced (after watching the Olympics) that with a few lessons and a little practice, they too will be competing for the gold. Dreams may not always match the reality of your job. You have to be honest with yourself. Being in a job for which you are ill suited (under- or over-qualified) leads to damaging results. Russ Hanlin talks a little about this. Russ has seen people struggle in jobs that were too much for them. He has watched as they lose their spirit, health, and, eventually, their jobs. He says he was honest enough with himself early in his career to realize that he wasn't a good entrepreneur. "There's a certain comfort I take in the corporate life and the structure of it. I guess I'm a corporate creature." Try to realistically match your dreams to your talent.

In any case, those who have a motive, natural drive, or something that needs expressing, but are not fulfilling it, are most probably stressed, to a degree. Selye says, "Deprivation of motivation is the greatest mental tragedy because it destroys all guidelines." By this he probably means that in lieu of pure motive, we create superficial motives that revolve around money and possessions. One becomes motivated to gain social approval for things accumulated rather than for inner fulfillment. Job enjoyment and mastery set a healthy work stage. One feels in control, competent, useful, and most often satisfied. By being attuned to our inner voice and thus our true motives, we can fulfill ourselves.

CHAPTER 7

STRESS-CONQUERING SKILLS

"Most of us live our lives in chains, unaware that we have the key."

Now it's time to get serious about this stress thing. It's time to learn the skills needed to free ourselves from the genetic, environmental, and psychological chains of stress.

Being informed about stress is important, but I find lack of information less of a problem for people than proper skills and motivation. Knowing everything there is to know about stress, including stress-conquering skills, is useless unless you are motivated to practice it with commitment and consistency.

STRESS IS A GREAT TEACHER

We spend a lot of energy avoiding stress—pushing it away or numbing ourselves from the effects of it. Unfortunately, most of our own solutions to stress turn out to be addictions. These addictions, whether drinking or shopping, blatant or subtle, don't solve anything and usually increase our level of stress by wearing away at our adaptation energy. Tempting as "stress novocaine" is, it doesn't teach us anything. It would be helpful if people could take the energy they use to push away stress and apply it to learning skills to manage stress.

While you may now view stress as something to get rid of so that you can get on with life, you may soon realize what a good friend and teacher stress can be.

Augie Nieto would agree. Augie says most of his life was spent "with my accelerator pedal to the floor." He says he now realizes there is a break pedal. Augie philosophizes, "Life is not a straight road; there are curves. When you come to a curve, there's the balance between the break and the accelerator in order to finesse the curve." "You don't think about the curves when you're young," he says. "Your glass is half full all the time. During my business career I didn't have a recession up until this one. I didn't know how to deal with it." He chuckles with chagrin as he continues, "My dad predicted the recession and I thought he didn't know what he was talking about. He was right…I get older—he gets smarter."

INTERNAL AND EXTERNAL STRESS-CONQUERING SKILLS

Our goal is to change our relationship with stress, both internally and externally. Chapters 8 and 9 break down the Stress-Conquering Skills into two categories: Internal Skills and External Skills. As we have learned, we need to work on controllable, external factors to help us modify stress, and we also need to work on an internal level to monitor our reaction to uncontrollable stressors, to achieve peace of mind, and to gain insight.

External methods such as exercise, talking with friends, or reading, can do wonders in modifying the effects of stress, but they don't teach us skills for ongoing or unavoidable stresses. They can sometimes actually keep us from the more intimate, often tougher, job of self-examination. Then again, not everyone is open to, or ready for, this kind of work, so you must choose the skills that best suit you.

Sometimes it's a good idea to remove yourself from your stressful surroundings. Take a vacation and change the scene, if only for a day. Other times it's possible and appropriate to make logistical changes to eliminate stressors that are in your face. And finally, it is invaluable to learn internal skills, skills that allow you to stride effortlessly through stress so that it is actually no longer defined as stress but just another aspect of life to be experienced with equanimity.

The external and internal skills that are fully discussed in Chapters 8 and 9 are summarized here.

External Skills

1. Time management and organizational skills
2. Set stress-resistant boundaries for yourself
3. Money management skills
4. Touch therapy for less stress
5. Create a creative outlet
6. A pet is less expensive than a therapist
7. Humor and play for less stress
8. Exercise for less stress
9. Eat right for less stress

Internal Skills

1. Vipassana meditation
2. Head-to-toe relaxation exercise
3. Contraction-release relaxation exercise
4. Breathing exercises: Breathe your way through stress
5. Visualization exercises for less stress

CHAPTER 8

NINE EXTERNAL STRESS-CONQUERING SKILLS AND TIPS

"You have to delegate. You can't do it all yourself."

—Russ Hanlin, CEO, Sunkist

ONE Time Management and Organizational Skills

Feeling you have no control over your time, always running behind, or forgetting appointments causes stress. Having your desk, home, and life piled high with projects, mess, and confusion also causes stress. Most everybody could use help in this area and could decrease their level of stress by managing time better and being more organized in general.

Efficiency comes naturally to Augie Nieto. Needing only three to four hours of sleep gives Augie an advantage in fitting it all in, but he still has his tricks. While riding his Lifecycle at 4:30 A.M., Augie gets a lot of his reading done—time management was one of the things Augie had in mind when he founded Life Fitness. Exercisers can read while getting their exercise.

Meyer Gottlieb of Samuel Goldwyn has some interesting time-saving tricks. For example, he uses the telephone for meetings rather than "scheduling a big two-hour meeting." He does lunches only when he thinks it's the most effective way of communicating with that person. In general, Meyer believes there are too many memos and extra paper work in companies. He says, "We're drowning in paper in this country. We're not doing the planet any good and we're not doing ourselves any good from an efficiency standpoint."

Traffic jams don't bother Meyer because, "If it's busy, it's busy. There's nothing that can be done." But when Meyer sees time being squandered, it bothers him. Laughing as he makes his point, he says, "For example, when you go into a post office, it's a time warp; it's 1931. People are actually still licking the stamps and so forth. I try not to go there." He adds, "I also don't go into banks. I use the automatic machines."

Augie's corporate advice on time management is simple: hire the best people. He has learned the hard way that the wrong person takes more of your time in that you don't fully relinquish control. He says, "You try to micromanage it, which is time consuming and stressful."

Interestingly, Meyer Gottlieb admits he has a little trouble with job delegation, but it's actually in the interest of time management. He says, "I figure I can just do it myself faster by the time I tell them."

Russ Hanlin found delegation difficult too, but believes in it. Russ delegates, but just as importantly, he follows up on the things he delegates. "I keep a very active suspense file on the things I delegate, and each morning I check my list for follow-ups," he says.

Augie thinks it's important to learn how to prioritize and it is his current challenge. He knows that better prioritization helps him handle the influx of demands that cross his desk each day.

You need some kind of time schedule and you need some system of organization and list making whether you work at home or in an office. This does not have to be a complex system of cross-referenced data. Most people do quite well with a simple file system, a daily activities calendar and a "to-do" list. Russ Hanlin of Sunkist keeps a "to-do" calendar but says he also has an "inner clock" that helps him manage his time. "It's kind of an inner sense of what has to be done rather than scheduling." For example, if he knows he's tightly booked for the day, he is "extremely efficient" and avoids "small talk and kidding around." In contrast, if his schedule is not so tight, he will take more time to promote the relationships with people and catch up on other company issues. Russ' travel tips for time management? "Bring a briefcase full of things to do with otherwise wasted time."

Take the little time it requires to get educated and organized in managing your time and adapt a daily system that works for you. This first step will help you with career success, personal success, and stress success by allowing you the needed time for each.

TWO Set Stress-Resistant Boundaries for Yourself

Learn to protect and physically separate yourself from those controllable factors that cause you stress, including stressful people, places, or things. Reassess what causes you stress (remember, *identify your stressors*). We often get into ruts or situations that seem unavoidable and aren't fully conscious of what causes us stress, or we may forget we have a choice. Choose to get out of that rut and separate yourself from negative or stressful surroundings when possible.

"Downloading" for less stress. Each CEO I interviewed for this book had his own way of protecting himself from stress. For example, Augie says he's learning to compartmentalize his thoughts. "If a problem can't be immediately resolved, the secret is to put it down in a place where you know you can come back to it. Then you don't have to worry about, 'Where's that thought?' "

Meyer also uses this technique and refers to it as "downloading." "When I'm working, I'm working, but when I leave, I turn it off. That's it," he explains. "It's subconscious. I just turn the computer off and store it somewhere in the back of my brain, in inactive memory." Meyer also uses a real computer and an assistant because, like Augie, he says, "It's very important that I know it's some place where I can retrieve it. Then I don't have to think about it."

THREE Money Management Skills

Financial problems cause stress, and most of us have them. They are a leading cause of divorce. Learn a little about money management. Pick up a book on the subject or ask a friend who is experienced in this area. As with time management, you do not have to develop a complex system. Simply take the time to establish a financial plan; then stick to that plan, no matter what.

FOUR Touch Therapy for Less Stress

As you now know, stress gets locked up in our bodies and causes more stress. The power of touch has been well-documented from helping incubator babies and comatose patients to simple stress reduction.

Massage is a good way to release bound up negative energy (incurred by stress) in your body by manually relaxing the muscles to allow full energy flow to all parts of the body.

If you can't afford a massage, think about touching and being touched more. Remember the hug craze of the '80s? I never got into hugging strangers, but the concept is valid. With those whom you feel comfortable, you might exchange one-minute shoulder massages right at your desk.

Besides relaxing muscles, I believe there is a tangible field of positive energy that is transferred through touch that is therapeutic for body and soul.

FIVE Create a Creative Outlet

Do you have a creative streak? Think before you answer because it may have been dormant for so long that you've forgotten, or you may never have known it existed. Develop anything you have an interest in, with no thought of monetary reward. Something you enjoy that will let your imagination and creative energy go. It may be something as simple as organizing your closet, creating a garden or a recipe, or even repairing things around the house. Russ Hanlin is a skilled mechanic and handyman and enjoys the creative challenge of repairing things himself. Russ also enjoys "digging around" in his garden and playing his piano and guitar for a creative release. He says, "I really relax by playing a musical instrument. I can get lost in that for a half hour and get rid of all my cares."

Don't check *Webster's* on this one. Do whatever makes you feel alive. This is particularly important if you don't have a job that fulfills this need.

SIX A Pet Is Less Expensive Than a Therapist

I had resisted owning a pet for years, until my sister Pat tricked me into babysitting a school-abused little bunny named Lassiter. (Pat, a psychologist, knew I wanted one but would never make the decision unless pushed.) A year-and-a-half later I realize that one of my favorite stress reducers is this little hopping ball of fur. He hops under my desk at just the right time in search of his own touch therapy. No matter how immersed I may be in the day's business, there has not been one night that I haven't smiled or laughed out loud as I watch Lassiter trailing me to my room, hopping as fast as he possibly can, ears askew.

According to *Medical World News*, those acute care facilities that allow animal visits are associated with patients' shorter recovery times, lower heart rates, and less requests for pain medication. Pets affect us physiologically as well as psychologically. Because of their unconditional love, they are good stress therapy.

SEVEN Humor and Play for Less Stress

While Meyer Gottlieb kids around in the office, he knows that he doesn't get enough personal play time. But he is working on it and promises, "It's one of the projects I have for myself."

As with pet ownership, research documents the positive effects of humor and play. Those who laugh and have a sense of humor have been shown to recover from an illness faster than those with a stiff, humorless approach to life. The changes are physical as well as mental: Physiological responses last up to 45 minutes after a good laugh. Catacholamines are released that activate the immune system and endorphins, causing an overall feeling of well-being.

One of Russ Hanlin's forms of play and relaxation is crossword puzzles. He describes himself as an "inveterate crossword puzzle guy." When he travels he takes a few with him that his wife has cut out from the newspaper. "They help put me to sleep in a hotel room."

Humor and play are usually the first things to go in a stressful situation, especially when the situation is uncontrollable. In the spring of 1991 Minnesota farm crops were demolished by rain and resulting floods. It was disastrous. Spirits were down or nonexistent. In the midst of this tragedy the *Minneapolis Tribune* ran a photo of a farmer water skiing on what used to be his field. That picture was worth at least 1,000 laughs, I'm sure. If life deals you lemons....

EIGHT Exercise for Less Stress

> *"Those who don't find time for exercise will have to find time for illness."*
>
> —*Old Proverb*

In fact, less active people have a 52 percent chance

of developing hypertension. Exercise reduces stress and makes you feel good physically and mentally. In one study, exercise relieved depression in 75 percent of the patients tested. It's pretty simple. Many of the executives I interviewed for both this book and another use exercise as a significant part of their stress therapy.

Exercise helps unleash energy that is lodged in the body in the form of tension. It gets trapped energy moving again, creating a healthful flow throughout the body.

The health benefits of exercise are numerous and impressive but are not the focus of this book. Simply remember that if your body is healthy and strong, your overall immunity to stress is increased.

NINE Eat Right for Less Stress

You should be aware that unhealthful foods cause stress in your body. Nutritional stress irritants include the obvious: fats, caffeine, and sugar (sugars account for 18 percent of our caloric intake). They also include the less obvious, such as foods to which you may be allergic.

You must learn to read your body's stress signals regarding nutritional irritants and eliminate them before they become habits (we often crave foods to which we are sensitive). Try changing your ideas about food. For example, instead of saying "I love a nice, juicy burger," practice saying, "I love a delicate, grilled salmon."

When I asked the CEOs in this book about their diets, their response could be summarized in one word: balance. Augie Nieto says, "The more I exercise the more I eat and vice versa. I keep a balance."

Make a moderate but specific commitment to eating right for less stress and keep track of it on a monthly calendar. Regularly upgrade your goals.

CHAPTER 9

FIVE INTERNAL STRESS-CONQUERING SKILLS

"Though one should conquer a million men in battlefield, yet he, indeed, is the noblest victor who has conquered himself."

—Dhammapada

So what exactly is our role in conquering stress? What happens when sickness, injury, or age prevents you from implementing your usual external stress eliminators such as exercise or getting away for the weekend? Generally, it's not a pretty picture.

SELF-MASTERY FOR LESS STRESS

The battle with stress is won, to a large extent, within. The skills described here encompass your internal stress gauges, including psychological and emotional states.

At first some of the techniques may seem awkward, but with practice they will become second nature. It will also become second nature to know which skill to apply when. Remember these skills are very real; they change the way our bodies react to stress. Some can even affect involuntary physiological functions (like blood pressure and heart beat). In the '60s this was considered impossible.

MEDITATION BRINGS STRESS TO ITS KNEES

Meditation and relaxation techniques are some of the most powerful skills you can possess in conquering stress. Meditation has been shown to cause physiological changes in the body, such as lowering blood pressure and reducing pain. Meditation also lowers the level of lactate in your system. (Lactate increases with stress and is responsible for making you feel anxious, although there are those who argue this point.) Stress is hypermetabolic; it speeds us up. Meditation is hypometabolic; it slows us down.

Results of meditation research are numerous and far-reaching. For example, the recidivism rate of prisoners who were taught meditation techniques at San Quentin was 35 percent to 40 percent lower than among former convicts who had received vocational training, prison education, or psychotherapy. This study was published in 1987 in the *Journal of Criminal Justice* and reported in *The Los Angeles Times* in an article appropriately titled, "Meditation: Into the Cells of the Mind."

Internal techniques like meditation and imagery are a little like having your own built-in biofeedback system. Biofeedback is based on two main principles. One principle says that every change in your mental-emotional state is accompanied by an appropriate change in your physiological state (body), whether conscious or unconscious, and vice versa. The other principle says that any (neurophysiological) function that can be monitored and fed back to a person through any of his five senses can be brought under voluntary control by that person (Green, Green & Walters, 1969). This is pretty exciting information that can help you build a powerful stress immunity system.

Meditation helps you get out of your own way. Meditation does more than reduce stress. Meditation helps connect you to every cell in your bodymind. It opens up long dormant lines of communication between your conscious and unconscious minds, integrating the psychological with the physiological.

Meditation has a carry-over effect that diffuses the ongoing effects of stress. Vipassana teacher Shinzen Young often says that vipassana meditation "rewires your nervous system." In fact, meditation has been shown to relieve nervous system stress more efficiently than sleep. (You can be asleep and yet very tense; consider those people who grind their teeth all night, or awaken with a migraine in the morning.)

The fact that meditation improves your ability to concentrate is another story, but one that is relevant to your success in whatever you do. It helps you to quiet external as well as internal noise; it quiets the ever-churning mind as well as outside distractions so you can better focus on the job at hand.

Although the '90s are a time for introspection, meditation is still much underutilized. Try the meditation/relaxation techniques described below. You might want to record your voice reading the description. Should you want a bit more direction, refer to my guided meditation tapes in the back of this book.

ONE Vipassana Meditation

Surrender to stress and you will conquer it. How do you surrender to stress? By first clearly identifying where stress is locked up in your body. By experiencing everything about it, welcoming it with open arms, and not pushing it away, you surrender to it. Your focus is not on thinking and talking about some outside stress monster, but on feeling your internal reactions to it. You can surrender to sickness and even death in the same way.

When you apply the vipassana technique, you no longer have to experience the symptoms of stress in the same negative way. Instead, they can be experienced with equanimity and insight. You demystify stress and thus no longer react in the same way.

Vipassana Meditation

1. Sit in a comfortable position (but not so comfortable that you will fall asleep).
2. Starting with your forehead, ask yourself where the tension is, however subtle or gross. Identify the area specifically. (If you like, try this right now for 10 to 30 seconds).
3. Describe everything about this area of tension aloud or to yourself:
   - How intense is it on a scale of one to 10?
   - How big is it?
   - What are its boundaries?
   - How far does it penetrate?
   - What color is it?
   - How else could you describe it?
     (Try this now for 10 to 30 seconds)
   - Now how intense is it on a scale of 1 to 10?
4. While you are examining the tension, maintain an open attitude. Let the area around you soften, and release your primal hold on the tension. Dive into the area and let the energy break up and spread through your body. (Try this now).
5. Now move to the eyes and do the same thing, then the jaw joint muscles, cheeks, mouth area, neck, shoulders, chest, stomach, abdomen, thighs, calves, feet, and toes. Be patient and concentrate on each area long enough to feel everything and anything about it—the skin against your clothes, the muscles, and even the organs, as you get more proficient. Be patient and pause long enough to really make contact. (Try this now with any part of your body. For example, how does your face feel right now? Are you holding tension around your eyes? Your jaws? Your mouth? Soften and release, as you describe those areas, one at a time. Now enjoy that feeling of complete release for a moment before reading on).

Stress is not an enemy that you wrestle to the ground. It is best defeated by pulling it out from under the carpet and exposing it to death.

At some point during vipassana meditation, you will see the tension start to break up or at least change. Keep watching, it's interesting—similar to watching your own private closed-circuit television program featuring *you* (what could be more interesting?). Watch that area with complete objectivity and equanimity and with no attachment to results. (Don't say, "This will get rid of my stress in ten minutes.") The whole idea of vipassana meditation is that whatever is happening is okay; stress or pain is part of life and something to be experienced fully. And of course, it is precisely this attitude, a nonaversive one, that diffuses the power of negative experience and eventually releases us from its grasp. The stressor or pain may still be present in a technical sense, but since our experience of it and approach to it are different, it changes forms inside us.

It is really quite a fascinating experience when you first realize that you have experienced a formerly negative situation with complete openness. The limitations of your paradigms become very apparent in an insightful sort of way.

While you should try to do formal sitting practice everyday for 10 to 30 minutes, it is a practice that is meant to be applied every minute of every day to the extent you are capable. As stress arises on a daily basis, learn to tune inward to your bodily reactions even before you try "fixing it" externally. You'll become aware when your shoulders start to tighten and raise up. You'll simply observe the tension and let the shoulders soften and relax all in just a few seconds while sitting at your desk. You'll become skilled at detecting stress and all other feelings such as anger, confusion, and tiredness in your body. You'll be surprised at how many things may not even need external action after applying vipassana.

Vipassana "right now" exercise: Here is a quick, effective exercise to apply throughout your day that will demonstrate the effectiveness of vipassana meditation. Take three deep breaths and relax. Now think of a recent stressful event. Visualize your boss yelling, deadlines due, or being in a traffic jam when you are late for an important appointment. Really try to *be* there as if it is happening right now. Bring it back to life. Take your time. Now, put the scene on hold and turn your focus to the sensations in your body. Exactly where do you feel that stress in your body? Don't think too much, just let your body answer. Your head? Your stomach? Wherever it is, congratulations, you have just taken your first big step toward identifying stress in the body, exposing it, and thus, conquering it.

For everyday use, you would simply pause in a particularly stressful situation and ask yourself where you feel the external stressor manifesting inside your body. You then apply the regular vipassana skills as described above. Feel the stress fully, surrender to it, and watch it dissolve. Eventually you will automatically become aware of negative body sensations and tend to them as they come up.

TWO Head-to-Toe Relaxation Exercise

1. Sit or lie in a comfortable position with soft music or nature sounds playing, if you like.
2. Starting with the head, relax every muscle in your body inch by inch, slowly moving down your body to your feet. Pause 10 to 30 seconds on each part of your body as you allow it to relax more and more. Be aware of the muscular tension in each area and let it release its controlling grasp on you and the world. Start with the forehead, then move to the eyes, jaw, cheeks, neck, shoulders, and continue slowly down your body.

3. This exercise usually takes 15 to 20 minutes but can be done in quickie one-to-five minute sessions as you become proficient. Combining Head-to-Toe relaxation with a little visualization, you might now feel a cleansing waterfall wash over and through your body from head to toe, relaxing you as it carries away the toxins of stress. (See "Visualization" at the end of this chapter.)
4. This is an effective technique to use for falling asleep. You will usually wake up in the morning trying to guess what body part you left off with, since you almost never make it to your feet.

THREE Contraction-Release Relaxation Exercise

1. Lie in a comfortable position, with soft music playing if you like.
2. Curl up your toes and contract both feet as tightly as you can and hold for 10 seconds.
3. Release your feet and feel the sensations of relaxation fill both feet for 5 to 10 seconds.
4. Move up your body, isolating part by part, contracting-holding-releasing your calves, thighs, buttocks, stomach, chest, shoulders, arms, and finally face. Be sure to tense only *one* area at a time, leaving every area around it as relaxed as you can. When you've finished the whole body, feel and enjoy the flow of energy thoughout. You have just released energy trapped as bodily stress and you will feel refreshed and revived. This exercise teaches your body the difference between tension and relaxation. Most of us carry tension around in our bodies without knowing it, even when we're ostensibly relaxing. And remember that trapped energy leads to illness, so you are doing more than just relaxing here, you are maintaining a healthy flow of your vital lifeforce energy.

FOUR Breathing Exercises: Breathe Your Way Through Stress

Proper breathing eliminates stress; improper breathing creates stress. When we are under stress our muscles tighten up, including those responsible for full breathing. When stressed, we breathe in a shallow, paradoxical manner; we breathe more from the chest and less from the abdomen. This restricts the oxygen intake to our brain. The worst part is that this "stress breathing" gets to be a habit and we start to breathe in a restricted way most of the time. Dull, fuzzy thinking and tiredness are two results of "stress breathing" that often lead to even more stress.

To feel what proper breathing is like, lie on your stomach and relax for a few minutes. Soon you will feel the abdomen expanding and contracting rhythmically. Then slowly roll over and lie on your back, continuing to be aware of the full expansion of the lungs, from bottom to top.

You should first learn what correct breathing is, then practice it daily until it becomes your natural way of breathing. Start to be aware of how your breathing pattern changes when you are stressed. See how the patterns affect your mind and body.

The Complete Breath

1. Inhale slowly to the count of 12, filling the lungs from bottom to top. Really stretch those lungs toward the end of the inhalation, squeezing in every ounce of air you possibly can. Try not to tense your neck and shoulders as you inhale.
2. Hold for a slow count of 8 to 12.
3. Exhale slowly to a count of eight. Be sure to exhale fully, exaggerating the contracted motion.
4. Practice this lying down until it becomes quite natural. Then try breathing this way while sitting, standing, and walking. Take a complete breath or two at a

stop light, between phone calls, waiting in lines or in traffic, in an elevator, and in meetings.

Breath Awareness Exercise

This is the simple practice of being aware of your breath as it enters and exits your body. This exercise can also be used as meditation by repeating it for five to thirty minutes.

1. Put your attention at the base of your nostrils, just above the lip where you can feel the air come and go.
2. Now, just watch that spot as you inhale and exhale. Don't try to control your breath, just observe it. "Ride" your breath in and out like a surfboard. In the pauses between inhalation and exhalation, keep focusing on that same spot, like staring at a spot on the wall.
3. Experiment with a continued form of this exercise: Count to 5 and down again: 1—inhale, exale, 2—inhale, exhale.... When you reach 5, reverse and count down 4, 3, 2, 1. Then start over again. Don't be discouraged when your mind wanders. Keep returning to your counting and try to stay focused as long as you can. See how far you can get without losing your concentration. You will feel quite relaxed and centered when you finish. This is also a very effective exercise for building concentration.

Exercise is a great opportunity to apply the Breath Awareness Exercise. Establish your own rhythm as you run, lift weights, swim, or work out on Augie's Lifecycle. For example, inhale for four counts while taking four steps on the stair machine. Then exhale and count the same way. What was mere exercise becomes a very focused, insightful, and complete meditation experience—a joining of body and mind.

FIVE Visualization Exercises for Less Stress

Imagery, or visualization, is not just an exercise for the mind—it can make real changes in the body. It can alter skin temperature, blood pressure, and muscle tension. In sports it has been demonstrated that an injured player who is unable to practice can experience the benefits of practice by just visualizing his practice. Small electrical changes can be detected in the muscles associated with the image, even though there is no actual movement of that muscle. In other words, muscles can be trained mentally, without movement! If you watch sports, you will often see an athlete such as a diver pause for a few seconds before beginning. He is rehearsing the dive, "experiencing" it one last time in his mind, getting his body and mind primed for what is about to happen.

Augie Nieto says he visualizes where he and his company are going. He says, "I think it's important. It's no different than the athlete who is going to run the 100-yard dash."

You might want to tape your own relaxing visualization or memorize a scene that works best for you.

- Get in a comfortable sitting or lying position and, using one of the techniques described above, relax for two to three minutes. Just taking a few deep breaths will do.
- Visualize a scene or image that best represents sheer relaxation to you. *Be* there in the scene.

Examples of Visualization

- A scene — Take your own 1- to 20-minute mini-vacation. See yourself on your own private beach, all alone. See the details: Are there birds? Whitecaps? Clouds? Sun? See the white sand, what you are wearing, and the peaceful look on your face. Let yourself sink into the warm sand as the sun melts away your stress and tension. Let time stand still; leave the past and future on hold. Feel your head, warm and relaxed, your neck and shoulders, loose and pain free. Feel your right arm in the sand, heavy and relaxed. Move through your entire body in the same way.

- An image — Feel a magical, cool waterfall washing over your head and face, cleansing away the toxins of stress. Feel it flowing over your shoulders and arms, gushing through your torso, reopening channels of energy as it runs down into your legs. See all the tension being released through your toes. See what the toxins actually look like as they are being carried out. Then see your whole body flowing with clean, clear-flowing energy, just like your magical, healing waterfall. Feel it flowing freely in your arms, in your face, all through your body. Enjoy the sensations and know that you can bring them up whenever you want.

CHAPTER 10

PSYCHOLOGICAL SKILLS FOR CONQUERING STRESS

Master self, master stress.

While meditation, relaxation, and visualization skills talk to your bodymind in subtle ways, retraining your reaction to stress, psychological skills deal more directly with your mental and emotional makeup. Besides those listed below, remember to implement other psychological skills we've already covered, such as challenging your paradigm.

HOW TO COMMUNICATE FOR LESS STRESS

How to Self-Dialogue

All of us have an ongoing internal dialogue with ourselves all day long. The problem is that most of this dialogue is negative. The idea behind Self-Dialoguing is that you learn to first catch the negative, stressful dialogue in process. You then challenge it, and finally you replace it with positive dialogue.

There are many "sub-selves" in us that want different things at different times; these may include: the parent self, the inner child who is always looking to replace parts of an unfulfilled past, the rebellious teenager, and the wiser self. We must learn to listen to all of these voices, these parts of ourselves, and not be judgmental about them. But let your wiser self direct the meeting. Self-Dialoguing is like sitting down to have a compassionate but serious business meeting with "your selves." When you are stressed, learn to stop and have a talk outloud with yourself (your car is a perfect private setting for this).

Ask yourself exactly what is causing you stress. Let any one of your selves answer, thus *identifying the stressor.* Then let both selves discuss how you might best resolve it. Don't judge the scared, stressed one for feeling that way ("It's silly that I'm feeling stressed. This is not a big issue."). Talk it through and encourage this self to express every seemingly insignificant aspect of the stressful issue at hand. Even if no clear-cut resolution is achieved, you will feel better for honoring all selves and getting those dark, insidious feelings out in the open.

Sometimes you'll land on one phrase that helps you with perspective. As a teenager, when I was worried about a test or some other high school trauma, I remember my dad putting it in perspective with one question, "What's the worst thing that could happen?" If he saw I needed one more nudge, he would add dramatically (but effectively), "Are you going to lose your legs or arms? No? Then what's the problem?" Suddenly feeling lucky to not be losing my legs and arms (or anything else), the upcoming trauma was reduced to proper molehill size. I still use this what's-the-worst-thing-that-could-happen technique to reduce stress from worrying.

How to Communicate with Others Stresslessly

Lack of communication or poor communication with others is a major source of stress in our personal and professional lives. Sunkist CEO Russ Hanlin encourages employees who have shut themselves off to share their feelings with coworkers.

Augie Nieto has good corporate communication skills but says personal communication has been more difficult. "I handle business adversity better than I do personal. I learned about business in school but I never learned about personal relationships," he says. Personal communication is something he is working on and advises, "You need to communicate what you're going through to your wife and kids. Don't just say you're overloaded. Tell them why, take them through it."

Skill in communication can be complicated because so many issues come into play, such as faulty paradigms and an imperfect language. We try to cram all thoughts and feelings into an arbitrarily selected group of words. Even if we were language scholars, this is too often a fool's errand. I am reminded of the limitations of language whenever I talk with people who are multilingual. They often grab a phrase from another language for want of finding it in the present one. However, some basic communication principles can go a long way, such as:

1. **Listen.** Really try to hear what the other person is trying to communicate. Let go of your compulsive urge to say what feels so important to you at the time. (Use the vipassana skill and feel where the urge to talk manifests itself in your body, and let it dissolve).
2. **Switch paradigms.** Try to understand the other person's point of view or why he believes what he is saying. Don't be judgmental when speaking. You turn listeners off when you use judgmental black-or-white language. Try to expand your paradigm; be open-minded: "I understand what you're saying and why you feel that way."
3. **Be diplomatic,** but say what you mean. Don't talk in circles. For example, learn to say "no."

HOW TO DESENSITIZE YOURSELF FROM STRESS

Give yourself a comfort zone challenge once in a while. Assign yourself a lesser version of the event that makes you stressful. Apply the stress reducing skills of your choice as outlined here. Increase the challenge as you become more desensitized. Thinking of them as exercises will help diffuse the stress, and the planned practice will eventually desensitize you to the stressor when it comes up in "real life." For example, if the idea of deadlines creates stress for you, assign yourself a series of manageable deadlines. Increase the difficulty with each assignment.

HOW TO LET IT OUT: STRESS-RELEASING EXERCISES

The following are invaluable exercises that use a physical approach to release negative energy. I know people who do these exercises on a daily basis, if only for a few minutes. Be willing to try all of the following exercises, then pick the ones that work best for you. Most people don't resort to doing stress-releasing (or emotion-releasing) exercises unless they are desperate, claiming that they aren't stressed about anything. The truth is we all carry some level of stress, in the form of negative emotions, around with us most of the time, even though it may not show. If you think about what is causing you stress, you will usually find some anger, depression, frustration, guilt, fear, or other negative emotion connected with it. These emotions cause stress and rob us of our (adaptation) energy by holding it hostage in our bodies where it can eventually cause harm. Just start punching on a cushion as hard as you can for 30 seconds and you'll see what lurks beneath. Don't think about what's happening, just do it. Then feel the release of energy that follows.

Commit to giving the following exercises a fair try for a month. Keep track on your time management calendar.

Five Stress-Releasing Exercises

1. Yell—in your car or into a pillow if circumstances require. Say whatever words come out or just make sounds. Try to keep it up for at least 30 seconds.
2. Hit, squeeze, or kick—anything that feels right and doesn't cost you anything. Hit a cushion or your bed with your fist or a racket, throw things, stomp your feet. Keep it up for one to three minutes. Then rest. Repeat.
3. Exercise. As you ride your Lifecycle, run, or hit a tennis ball against a backboard, exaggerate the activity with full force and let out anything and everything that's trapped inside.
4. Breathe with movement. Use your breath in an exaggerated way while imitating karate-type punching or kicking moves into the air (versus against a surface). Exhale strongly with the effort, either silently or with a karate-type yell.
5. Turn everyday tasks into an exercise. Select an activity that you will execute with focused intent on releasing negative emotions. For example, bat a rug with unleased energy; polish your car; or scrub the floor.

SUMMARY

WHEN STRESS HITS: THE SIX STEPS TO CONQUERING STRESS

When you first realize that you are beginning to experience stress, or think you might, here is a summary of the steps you should take to conquer stress. For an ever-improving reaction to stress, practice these steps on a daily basis.

Psychological

1. Self-dialogue. Talk out loud. Play your own psychologist. Use Self-Dialoguing to: (a) acknowledge that you are stressed; (b) define the source of your stress, if possible, and (c) find a solution or reach a temporary resolution about the stresses that all selves are in agreement with. Respect your stress-related negative emotions (frustration, anger, depression). Realize, however, that your emotions are based on your perspective (past experiences and ideas) of things and that things are not always as they seem. Drop your paradigm for a moment and try on the opposing point of view. If Self-Dialoguing is difficult for you, talk to a friend or even a professional counselor. This first step may eliminate your negative emotions altogether or at least take the edge off.

Logistical:

2. Control stress. Where possible, get control of the things causing you stress. Pay your bills, change jobs, change relationships or whatever. Learn to prioritize and apply time management and organizational skills.

Physical

3. Exercise, stretch, and eat and drink healthful, non-aggravating things.

Emotional

4. Let it out. Use Stress-Releasing Exercises described above.

Energetic

5. Use Breathing Exercises, described above.
6. Use Vipassana Meditation skills described above. Especially effective for those things that can't be controlled (as well as a fuller experience of life, in general). I have found, for most clients, vipassana is potentially the most powerful exercise of all, with practice.

Feel exactly where the negative sensations of stress are located in your body. Circle it with an imaginary black magic marker. Now explore it to death. Look all around it and describe it as if you were telling a friend about it: how intense it is on a scale of one to ten; what color it is; how big it is; and anything else about it. Often the emotion or stress will partially or completely break up, and because of the complete way you experienced it, you will have actually gained insight and energy.

ADDITIONAL RESOURCES

Books

1. *Full Catastrophe Living: Using the Wisdom of Your Body and Mind to Face Stress, Pain, and Illness*, Jon Kabat-Zinn, Delta (New York), $12.00.
2. *Healing the Shame That Binds You*, John Bradshaw, Health Communications (Florida), $9.95.
3. *Healthy, Wealthy, and Wise: A Step-by-Step Plan for Success Through Healthful Living*, KRS Edstrom, Prentice Hall (Englewood Cliffs, NJ), $22.95.
4. *Minding the Body, Mending the Mind*, Joan Borysenko, Bantam Books (New York) $10.95.
5. *Quantum Healing: Exploring the Frontiers of Mind/Body Medicine*, Deepak Chopra, Bantam Books (New York), $10.
6. *The Relaxation Response*, Herbert Benson, Morrow (New York), $5.50.

Periodical

1. The American Institute of Stress *Newsletter*, (Yonkers, NY), $35/year.

Audiocassettes

1. "Five Classic Meditations," Shinzen Young, Insight Recordings (San Jacinto, CA), $7.95.
2. "Inner Mastery Series" (Relax Mind and Body/Defeat Pain/Conquer Stress/Sleep Through Insomnia/Your Base Meditation for Inner Mastery), KRS Edstrom, Get Motivated (Los Angeles), $48 series ($12 each).

INDEX

Adrenaline, 6, 9
Aging, 5
Alcoholism, 26, 43
Anabolic hormones, 6
Analytical mind, 57
Anger, 28–29
Anxiety, 17
Arehart-Treichel, Joan, 19
Aristotle, 16
Arteriosclerosis, 6
Arthritis, 13, 18
Asthma, 13, 34

Back pain, 14
"Bad Boss", 42–43
Bargh, John, 30
Belief systems. *See* Personal paradigms
Biofeedback, 81
Biorhythms, 24
Biotypes, 19
Blood pressure, 12, 80
See also Hypertension
Borkovec, Thomas, 27
Boundaries to stress, 74–75
Bradshaw, John, 30
Breathing exercises, 70, 87, 98

Camus, Albert, 62
Cancer, 13–14, 19–20
Cannon, Walter, 2, 6
Career stress, 64
Catabolic hormones, 6
Catecholamine, 77
Childhood, 29–30
Cholesterol, 6, 14–15
Chopra, Deepak, 51
Comfort zone, 59
Common cold, 14
Control, 58
Cornell University Medical College, 58
Cortisol, 6
Creative mind, 57
Creativity as stress relief, 70, 75–76
Crisis, 45–48

Depression, 29
Diabetes, 13
Diet, 70, 78
Disease prone personality, 17–20

Endorphins, 77
Environment, 22, 25–26
Eustress, 7
Exercise, 70, 77–78
Exhaustion, 7

Fatigue, 6
Forbes, Rosalind, 9

General Adaptation Syndrome, 5
Genetics, 22–24
Gottlieb, Meyer, 7–8, 25–26, 39, 41, 45, 65, 72–73

Hanlin, Russ, 2, 3, 8, 15, 23–24, 27, 43, 57–58, 62, 64–66, 73–74, 76–77, 93

Hardiness factor, 58
HealthStyle, 3, 52
Healthy, Wealthy, and Wise, 7, 62
Heart disease, 13–14, 18, 40, 58
Herpes, 13
Holmes, 2
Homeostasis, 6
Hormones, 5–6
Humor, 70, 77
Hypertension, 6, 13
Hypothalamus, 6

Identifying stressors, 53–57
Immune system, 6, 12, 77
Impotence, 14
Infertility, 14
Information overload, 39
Insomnia, 42
Institute of Applied Biology, 19
Irritability, 17

Job ambiguity, 40
Job satisfaction, 39
Journal of Criminal Justice, 81

King, Rodney, 56
Kritz-Silverstein, Donna, 40

LeShan, Lawrence, 19
Life Fitness, 7–8, 25, 38
Lippmann, Walter, 30
Listening skills, 94
Los Angeles riots, 56
Los Angeles Times, 81

Massage, 75
Medical World News, 76
Meditation, 80–85
  vipassana, 82–85, 98
Meyers, Gerald, 45
Migraine headaches, 9, 13, 18
Minneapolis Tribune, 77
Money management, 70, 75

New England Journal of Medicine, 14
Nieto, Augie, 7–8, 25, 29, 38–39, 41, 45, 63, 65, 69, 72, 78, 89, 94
Nietzsche, 22

Obesity, 13
Organizational skills, 70

Personal paradigms, 22, 30–36
Pets, 70, 76
Psoriasis, 13
Psychological characteristics, 22, 26–30
Psychoneuroimmunology, 15
Psychosomatic, 13, 15–16

Rahe, 2
Relationships, 26
Relaxation exercises, 70
  contraction-release, 86
  head to toe, 85–86
Respiratory diseases, 14
Rheumatoid arthritis, 18

Samuel Goldwyn, 7, 25–26, 39, 41, 65
Self dialogue, 92–93
Self esteem, 17, 26, 29
Selye, Hans, 2, 5, 7, 65–66
Siegel, Bernie, 20
Stress
  adaptation, 5
  addiction, 9

cognitive, 9–10
definition, 2, 7
emotional signs, 17
job related, 38–48, 62–66
noncognitive, 9–10
physical signs, 12–13
recovery from, 51–60
Stress-conquering skills, 59, 69–70
external, 70
internal, 70
Stress-conquering steps, 97–98
Stress related diseases, 13–14
Stress releasing exercises, 95–96
Stress scale, 2–3
Sunkist, 2, 8
Szent-Gyorgyi, Albert, 65

Technostress, 39
Time management, 70, 72–73
Touch therapy, 70, 75
Type A personalities, 24, 44

Ulcers, 6, 13, 18

Vipassana meditation, 70
See also Meditation
Visualization exercises, 70, 88–90

When It Hits the Fan, 45
Workaholics, 7
Worker's Compensation, 38
Worry, 26–28